THE · BUSINESS · SIDE · OF · GENERAL · PRACTICE

Making Sense of the New Contract

EDITED BY
JOHN CHISHOLM

WITH A FOREWORD BY
IAN BOGLE

RADCLIFFE MEDICAL PRESS
OXFORD

© 1990 Radcliffe Medical Press Ltd.
15 Kings Meadow, Ferry Hinksey Road, Oxford OX2 0DP

British Library Cataloguing in Publication Data

Making sense of the new contract.
  1. Great Britain. General practice. Finance
  I. Chisholm, John
362.1
ISBN 1-870905-55-5

Typeset by Advance Typesetting Ltd, Oxfordshire
Printed and bound in Great Britain

Contents

24. Supply of Drugs and Appliances   101

25. Undergraduate Medical Students   104

26. The Trainee Practitioner Scheme   105

27. The Doctors' Retainer Scheme   115

28. Postgraduate Education Allowance   116

29. Reimbursement of Rent and Rates   121

30. Improving Surgery Accommodation   131

31. Health Centres   147

32. Practice Staff   150

33. Computer Costs   157

34. Transitional Payments Scheme   160

35. Arrangements for Payment   161

36. Representations to the Secretary of State   164

37. How the Red Book is Negotiated and Implemented   165

     Appendices

     Index to the Statement of Fees and Allowances   169

     List of Abbreviations   178

     Parliamentary Regulations Affecting General Practice   179

     Index   185

Foreword

THIS book is essential reading for every GP. It has always been important that GPs should know what is required under the terms of service of their NHS contract and to understand how they should be paid for providing these services. This information is even more vital because of the contractual changes introduced last April.

During nineteen years as Secretary of the Liverpool Local Medical Committee, I have seen many cases of GPs unnecessarily experiencing difficulties simply because they have not understood what is required under their contract and how they should be paid for fulfilling these obligations.

This book is a vital reference document to be kept close to hand, which will help you and your staff to avoid these difficulties. Indeed, you may have to chain it down to ensure it can be readily found when needed!

IAN BOGLE
Chairman
General Medical Services Committee
British Medical Association

Making Sense of the New Contract

Contributors

PAUL BATES, *General Manager, Leicestershire Family Health Services Authority*

TIM BROWN, *Practice Manager, Sutton Coldfield*

NORMAN ELLIS, *Under Secretary, British Medical Association*

BILL ROBINSON, *General Manager, Suffolk Family Health Services Authority*

Editor

JOHN CHISHOLM, *Negotiator, General Medical Services Committee, British Medical Association*

The Business Side of General Practice

Editorial Board

Preface

NEW contractual arrangements for general practitioners were introduced on 1 April 1990. These constitute the most significant changes to the structure, ethos and morale of general practice since the implementation of the 1965 charter. But whereas the Family Doctor Charter was prepared by general practitioners, supported by the profession and negotiated with the government, the 1990 changes are being imposed on an unwilling profession. While the 1965 charter resulted in improved morale and increased recruitment to general practice, and provided a secure foundation for nearly 25 years of sustained development in primary care, there are already signs that the 1990 contract is producing disillusionment and a reduction in applications for places on GP vocational training schemes.

What is undeniable is that the introduction of the new contract has been extremely unsettling for general practitioners and health service administrators alike. So many contractual changes have been introduced, in the Regulations, the terms of service and the Statement of Fees and Allowances, that whatever the merits of those changes, and despite the concerted and angry professional opposition to their implementation, there is an urgent need for a simply expressed guide to the new contract. This book is intended to be that guide.

The Statement of Fees and Allowances (SFA) has for the last 24 years set out the basis on which general practitioners (GPs) are paid, and any GP who wishes to understand that system, and to learn how he or she is remunerated for services given to patients, needs to master the Red Book. However, the style of the Red Book is complex, daunting and densely legalistic, and as a result many doctors are unfamiliar with its contents, just as they are unfamiliar with the details of their contract with the Family Health Services Authority (FHSA) or Health Board.

This book is an attempt to explain the structure and principles of the new Red Book. Inevitably, even this book is sometimes quite complicated in expression, but it is to be hoped that it is much easier to read than the SFA itself. A deliberate decision has been taken to adhere to principles and broad outlines of the provisions of the Red Book rather than to consider fine detail, and in particular all references to current levels of fees and allowances have been excluded.

While the ordering of sections of the SFA is curious and to some extent accidental, with new sections being inserted wherever paragraphs have previously been unallotted, this book attempts to use a more logical sequence. However, a comprehensive index to the new Red Book is included, and should allow a reader to gain access to relevant paragraphs of the SFA much more quickly than can be achieved using the outline contents at the front of the Red Book itself. In addition, while paragraphs of the SFA are only referred to in the text of *Making Sense of the New Contract* when a reader is specifically directed to the detailed provisions of the Red Book, the index to this volume uses the same terms as are used in the separate index to the Red Book, so that a reader should easily be able to cross-refer from the text of this book to the detail of the SFA.

Readers must of course remember that only the original text carries the force of law and provides the detail needed for authoritative interpretation and resolution of any dispute as to meaning. The purpose of this book is different — it is to inform the reader of the broad structure of the Red Book and to give an overview of the complexity and range of general practitioners' fees and allowances.

One important matter of interpretation should be mentioned. While broadly speaking the contractual arrangements in Scotland are similar to those in England and Wales, the book does not make specific reference to the differences. The most important such difference is that in Scotland, GPs are in contract with Health Boards not Family Health Services Authorities.

The history of the Red Book

The Charter for the Family Doctor Service was published by the British Medical Association in March 1965. As a result of the successful negotiations that then took place between the Minister of Health and general practitioner representatives, the Regulations, terms of service and remuneration of GPs were all radically restructured. Regulation 22 of the National Health Service (General Medical and Pharmaceutical Services) Regulations 1966 (now Regulation 24 of the 1974 Regulations) placed upon the Minister of Health (now the Secretary of State for Health) an obligation to publish a statement of payments to doctors, and the Statement of Fees and Allowances was first published in October 1966. Although a surprisingly slim volume compared with the 1990 SFA, its structure and contents will seem surprisingly familiar to anyone acquainted with the modern Red Book. However, it was published as a booklet, and for the first few years amendments were issued to GPs via Executive Council Notices (ECNs). As a result, GPs soon found it hard to be certain of their entitlements.

Therefore in 1972 the loose-leaf, ring-bound version of the SFA was introduced, that is now so familiar as the Red Book. Subsequent amendments have been published as replacement or additional pages that allow a GP to maintain an up-to-date version of the Statement. The importance of ensuring that all SFA amendments are received and promptly incorporated into the Red Book cannot be emphasized too strongly. An out-of-date text is misleading and can lead to both false and overlooked claims.

At the end of 1989, a new Red Book was issued to all GPs, for the first time since 1972. This ensured that all GPs possessed a properly ordered, up-to-date Statement, defining the fees and allowances payable from 1 April 1990 under the new contractual arrangements.

In the past, amendments to the Red Book have been published at a rate of some nine a year, but often these have been confined to changes in one paragraph of the SFA, and have been quite brief. Already this year however, two lengthy and complex SFA amendments have been issued, and more are promised. The need for such significant amendments so early in the life of the new contractual arrangements has arisen from two causes: the haste with which the new contract was imposed, and the urgent negotiations that have taken place to ameliorate some of the worst features of the new arrangements.

Particularly significant amendments have been made to protect confidential personal information when claims are made for health promotion clinic fees, minor surgery session fees and cervical cytology target payments; to alter the arrangements for the direct reimbursement of trainee practitioners' medical defence organization subscriptions; to reimburse directly a wider range of computing costs; and to amend the procedures for representations to the Secretary of State.

As a result of these and other changes, the text of this book has required revision. In particular, the chapter on computer costs has been entirely rewritten and new sections have been added on 'opted out' doctors and on self supply and VAT registration.

Currently, there are unresolved disputes about the criteria for admission to the minor surgery list, and about whether target payments should be calculated on a partnership or individual list basis.

The profession meanwhile is monitoring the operation of the new contract, exposing its defects, striving to counteract any harmful effects on patients, and seeking improvements in the Regulations and the remuneration structure. For while the profession had long campaigned for remuneration for child health surveillance and minor surgery, for a registration fee, for deprivation payments, and for the direct reimbursement of computer costs, there remains strong opposition to important elements of the new contract – particularly the increased workload, the availability requirements, the health checks on patients who have not been seen within the last 3 years, the target payments scheme and the introduction of cash limits.

The Department of Health itself acknowledges that changes will be required in the light of experience of the new arrangements. Clearly therefore further SFA amendments of substance are inevitable.

The Business Side of General Practice

The original idea for a simple guide to the Statement of Fees and Allowances came from Stuart Carne. He discussed his proposal with Andrew Bax, the Managing Director of Radcliffe Medical Press, and from that initial suggestion has grown the idea for a series of books entitled The Business Side of General Practice. *Making Sense of the Red Book* was published last year, and the present book, which is essentially a radically revised second edition, is the second volume in the series.

It is envisaged that potential readers of such a series of books will not only include general practitioners, but also trainee practitioners, doctors' professional advisers and their ancillary staff, particularly practice managers, receptionists and all those involved in the administration of the doctor's office.

With such a readership in mind, an Editorial Board for The Business Side of General Practice was formed. It deliberately includes representatives of both the elected members and the secretariat of the General Medical Services Committee of the British Medical Association; a representative of the Royal College of General Practitioners; a Local Medical Committee secretary; a Family Health Services Authority general manager; and representatives of the Association of Health Centre and Practice Administrators and of the Association of Medical Secretaries, Practice Administrators and Receptionists. As a result, experts on terms and conditions of service, on training and education, and on the needs of readers, have been brought together to share their experience.

The initial and final chapters of *Making Sense of the New Contract*, which set the Statement of Fees and Allowances in its context by explaining independent contractor status, the Review Body system, the negotiating process and above all the Regulations and terms of service, have been written by Norman Ellis. The central section of the text, which expounds the content of the Red Book itself, has most appropriately been written by authors with experience of administering FPCs. Paul Bates, Tim Brown and Bill Robinson have all had day-to-day experience of advising doctors on the interpretation of the old SFA, and they have brought that wealth of past experience to bear in explaining the provisions of the new Red Book.

Acknowledgements

I am most grateful to all four contributors for the inestimable work they have done in bringing this project to fruition, and to the Editorial Board for their helpful comments on the initial drafts of the text.

I also wish to thank Michael Wilson, the immediate past Chairman of the General Medical Services Committee, for all the personal encouragement he has given me, and his successor Ian Bogle for writing the foreword to this book. Andrew Lockhart-Mirams of Hempsons Solicitors has provided invaluable service by compiling and updating the list of the Regulations, and Bill Roberts, former Assistant Secretary at the Department of Health and Social Security, who devised the loose-leaf format of the Red Book, has given me useful guidance concerning the history of the SFA.

There are three people to whom I am particularly grateful, for without their contributions this book would not have been produced. Stuart Carne fathered this book – his inspired initial concept has been fundamental to the whole project. Norman Ellis has been a model sub-editor, for he has both a mastery of English style and an intimate knowledge of the subject matter. Finally, Andrew Bax's cheerful enthusiasm, practical counsel and energetic commitment to this project, and the high production standards of the Radcliffe Medical Press, have been crucial in producing what I hope will be a valuable and helpful guide for all who wish to understand the basis of general practitioners' remuneration and of their new contract.

JOHN CHISHOLM
September 1990

1 Independent Contractor Status

AN independent contractor is a self-employed person who has entered into a contract of services with another party. This contract for services is fundamentally different from the contract of service which governs an employee–employer relationship. A key test, often used to distinguish between these two types of contract, relates to the question of 'control'. Generally, the more control A exercises over B's work, the more likely A is to be the employer and B the employee. Thus, if A can tell B not only what job to do but how it is to be done, A has sufficient control to make him B's employer.

However, if the exercise of control is much more diffuse, such that the person doing the work is not told how to do it, the contract is for services and the relationship is between what is confusingly known in legal terminology as 'the principal party' and an independent contractor. Obviously, this test is crude and there are borderline cases, but the status of the National Health Service (NHS) general practitioner (GP) as an independent contractor has not been seriously questioned in the past. As an independent contractor a GP should not be told by the Family Health Services Authority (FHSA) or Health Board how to practise. FHSAs and Health Boards should seek to persuade and advise, not direct or control.

The character of British general practice has been strongly influenced by the independent contractor status of its practitioners. The remuneration system, the organization of practices into partnerships, together with the medico-political institutions that enable GPs to exercise professional self-government, demonstrate this influence.

As independent contractors, GPs exercise discretion and freedom in how they run their practices. This autonomy carries with it the administrative and financial responsibility for running the business itself and also responsibility for the clinical services provided. These responsibilities include providing premises, staff and equipment. If GPs were health authority employees (like hospital consultants), the authority would be responsible for providing these resources.

The main advantages of an independent contractor service are its flexibility and adaptability, and the fact that it can offer a more personalized model of care. It also provides opportunities for innovation and diversity without interference, and gives patients scope for choice. Disadvantages may be apparent if the standards of service are allowed to vary widely; those who are responsible for administering GPs' contracts sometimes see this arrangement as untidy and unsatisfactory, because the means of control available to the employer are lacking.

No other occupation (apart from the other Family Health Services contractor professions – dentists, chemists and opticians) has this unique partnership with the State, or with the public. In current parlance, general practice is the original 'privatized' sector of the NHS. GPs in other Western developed economies, together with most other professionals, such as dentists, lawyers, architects, surveyors and accountants, are also independent contractors. In the United Kingdom, GPs have jealously guarded their independent contractor status ever since Lloyd George's national insurance scheme was introduced in 1911. The profession supported the idea of a State-funded medical scheme, but it was adamantly opposed to a salaried service; it recognized that the loss of independent contractor status would undermine the freedom of doctors to practise without State interference and ultimately put patient care at risk. GPs feared that government would seek to direct them in their day-to-day treatment of patients. This commitment to the independent contractor status underlies the policy of the Conference of Representatives of Local Medical Committees (LMCs).

The implementation of the new contractural arrangements is changing the relationship between individual GPs and the FHSA. New controls are being exercised by FHSAs over the work of GPs. The GP is now required to supply an annual report to the FHSA giving extensive information on the organization of the practice, prescribing arrangements and hospital referral statistics, and also to provide a more detailed statement of the hours he or she is available to patients for surgery consultations, health promotion clinics and home visits.

Additionally, the new arrangements specify more precisely the services GPs are required to provide for patients. The terms of service have been amended to make clear that health promotion and illness prevention fall within the definition of general medical services. The services that are required of the GP are spelt out in some detail, specifying which procedures should be undertaken and which patients should be offered certain services.

During the debate on the imposition of the new arrangements, the question has been raised as to whether the new Regulations and terms of service are incompatible with the GP's status as an independent contractor. Whilst there can be no doubt that greater control will now be exercised over the work of the GP, both the Government and the General Medical Services Committee (GMSC) of the British Medical Association (BMA) are agreed that the GP should continue to work as an independent contractor: indeed, in a joint statement from the Department of Health and the GMSC the Secretary of State for Health 'confirmed that the independent contractor status of GPs would not be affected'.

However the question of whether GPs are independent contractors is not something which can be resolved according to the wishes of the two parties directly concerned. It ultimately depends upon whether the control exercised by FHSAs is sufficiently diffuse to justify retention of the independent contractor status. In spite of the increased accountability required under the contract – and the increased powers of the FHSA – there should be no doubt that GPs continue to work as independent contractors. The old contract also contained detailed specification of certain clinical tasks (such as those relating to the provision of maternity care) and these have never been regarded as being incompatible with the independent contractor status.

2 How General Practitioners' Pay is Determined

THE Doctors' and Dentists' Review Body was set up in 1960, as a consequence of the recommendations of a Royal Commission known as the Pilkington Commission. Its remit is to recommend to the Prime Minister the levels of remuneration of doctors (and dentists) working in the NHS.

The Pilkington Commission was concerned to ensure that doctors' pay should not be used as a means of regulating pay movements in the economy; it wanted to see their pay removed from the political arena. The Commission considered various options, including direct negotiations, collective bargaining through Whitley machinery (used by most health service employees), and arbitration. It recommended an independent review body and laid down the ground rules by which it should operate (*see* Box 2.1).

Box 2.1: Ground rules of the Review Body

1 The Review Body's main task was to be the exercise of 'good judgement'
2 Although the Government had the ultimate power to decide, Review Body recommendations must only be rejected by Government very rarely, and for most obviously compelling reasons
3 Government should deal with Review Body recommendations promptly
4 The remuneration of doctors should be determined primarily, although not exclusively, by external comparison with other professionals and similarly qualified employees
5 Doctors should not be used by governments as part of their machinery for regulating the economy; they have a right to be treated fairly and the profession should assist the Review Body by willingly providing information about earnings
6 Doctors' earnings should not be determined according to short-term supply and demand considerations

---

How the Review Body system works

The Review Body is willing to receive evidence from any interested party, but in practice it concentrates on evidence from a few key sources (*see* Box 2.2, overleaf).

> **Box 2.2: Main sources of evidence to the Review Body**
>
> 1 Written evidence from the medical (and dental) profession, prepared by a committee of the BMA
> 2 Written evidence from the Health Departments
> 3 Joint written evidence agreed between the profession and the Health Departments, usually dealing with matters that have been agreed in negotiation
> 4 Jointly agreed statistical information, for example evidence on GPs' earnings and expenses
> 5 Independent evidence prepared by the Review Body's Secretariat, the Office of Manpower Economics, for example various surveys conducted at the request of the Review Body

Both sides, the professions and the Health Departments, normally submit written evidence to the Review Body on the same day and also exchange their documents. This means that each side has prepared its evidence 'in the dark', without sight of the other evidence.

The next stage involves oral hearings. The Review Body meets each side and uses the occasion as an opportunity to seek clarification of any subject raised in the written evidence or to discuss other points of concern. The parties will also use the oral hearing as an opportunity to emphasize or update any matter in their written evidence.

Having considered all the evidence, the Review Body reports in confidence to the Prime Minister. Further time usually elapses before the Prime Minister publishes the report and announces a decision on the recommendations.

General practitioners' remuneration

As independent contractors, GPs are paid a gross income by the NHS, out of which they meet practice expenses, including such items as staff salaries, the cost of providing surgery premises, and motoring expenses. The GPs' payment system is based on a principle known as 'cost plus'; the payments they receive are intended both to cover their expenses and to provide a net income.

The Review Body recommends what it considers to be an appropriate level of net income for GPs, and taking account of this recommendation the Government decides upon the average level of income of all GPs. In fact, individual GPs receive greatly varying amounts depending upon the particular circumstances of their practices; expenses and list sizes differ and GPs provide a varying range of services. Virtually all GPs earn either more or less than the average; it is exceedingly rare to find a GP whose earnings coincide with the average figure.

To the net income must be added the component for expenses. All expenses incurred by GPs in providing general medical services are paid back to the profession in full: some are paid directly to the individual GP who incurs them (these are known as directly reimbursed expenses); the remainder of GPs' expenses are reimbursed indirectly on an average basis through fees and allowances. Thus, the exact amount an individual GP receives in indirectly reimbursed expenses will not, except by pure chance, equal expenditure, and in practice, there will be a strong incentive for a GP to economize in respect of his or her own practice expenses.

Although this system of dealing with GPs' expenses is complicated and may lead to anomalies and inequalities, it does recognize the independent contractor status of the family doctor, which is fundamentally different from that of salaried colleagues employed elsewhere in the NHS. One possible alternative approach would have been to require each GP to submit to the FHSA a monthly or quarterly claim for expenses, which the FHSA would check (and no doubt question on occasion). If this arrangement had been adopted, the profession would have given up its independence to choose how to run its practices. The significance of this point is not always recognized by those who call for increased direct reimbursement.

It has been argued that because most practice expenses are repaid indirectly through fees and allowances, irrespective of what is spent, the less an individual GP spends on the practice the greater will be his or her profits. Although there is some truth in this view, it does not represent the whole picture. GPs are directly reimbursed for the cost of providing many of the most costly items (for example, surgery premises and practice staff). A GP who chooses to underfund his or her practice will find it lagging behind other practices in the services it can offer; it will not be as attractive to new patients and patients currently on the list may opt to change to other practices in the neighbourhood. A contrary and more positive view needs to be put forward. If those GPs who are unwilling to invest in their own practices would overcome their reticence, the profession as a whole would benefit through the indirect reimbursement system and general practice would become more capital intensive. For example, if every GP decided to invest in an ECG machine, the NHS would have no option but to fund this invest-ment through the indirect reimbursement scheme.

An explanation of how GPs' expenditure on defence body subscriptions is indirectly reimbursed illustrates this point. Almost every GP subscribes to a medical defence body, and traditionally the amount each GP pays has been almost the same. Thus, every GP is faced with a similar level of expenditure. These subscriptions have been paid ever since the present GPs' remuneration structure was established in the 1960s and therefore this expenditure is built into the system. The Review Body is aware that defence body subscriptions must be paid and that these have increased rapidly year by year. It is therefore able to make provisions for this expenditure in its estimates of GPs' expenses, including an element to take account of anticipated increases in the subscription rate. As almost all GPs pay this subscription, it is reimbursed through fees and allowances (and because future increases have been taken into account) at close to the prevailing rate.

Expenditure that is fully and directly reimbursed

Certain practice expenses are reimbursed directly to each GP. However, where the amount refunded is less than the total cost incurred by the GP, any remaining expenditure is claimed against income tax and is recorded subsequently as a part of those expenses to be reimbursed indirectly through the fees and allowances. Those items reimbursed directly and fully are listed in Box 2.3.

Box 2.3: Those items of a GP's expenditure that are reimbursed directly

1 Surgery rent and rates, water rates, water meter installation and charges, and refuse collection charges
2 Employer's national insurance contributions in respect of GP trainees and some practice staff
3 Employer's pension contributions in respect of GP trainees and certain approved schemes for practice staff
4 Net ingredient cost plus VAT of drugs dispensed under the drug tariff

---

Full direct reimbursement of all a GP's spending under any heading occurs only when the Government or some public agency has direct control over its costs, as is the case with national insurance contributions. Likewise, the GP receives full direct reimbursement of surgery rent if the rent is approved by a district valuer. Dispensing doctors are repaid 100% of the cost of the drugs they prescribe and dispense, because drug prices are effectively controlled by Government. A GP trainer receives full reimbursement for the trainee's salary and car allowance and employer's national insurance and super-annuation contributions, because again all these costs are within the control of Government.

Expenditure that is partially and directly reimbursed

The most common partial direct reimbursement is the refund of the salaries of practice staff. Examples of allowances with maximum or fixed ceilings include those relating to the employment of an assistant, employment of a locum to cover a GP's absence because of sickness, maternity or study leave, and payments made under the Doctors' Retainer Scheme.

The introduction of cash limits on the funds available to FHSAs for the direct reimbursement of the salaries of practice staff means that the percentage of the salary refunded in respect of future staff appointments may differ from the fixed rate of 70% reimbursement paid under the former ancillary staff scheme. FHSAs can now exercise discretion in determining the level of direct reimbursement, and thus it may vary from zero to 100%.

A new scheme for the partial direct reimbursement of computing costs is being introduced, and provides for the direct payment of a proportion of the costs of purchase, leasing, upgrading and maintenance of a computer system.

Expenditure that is indirectly reimbursed

As described above, each year the Review Body estimates on the basis of a survey of tax returns how much GPs as a body will spend on providing general medical services and then calculates an average figure for each GP. This figure is added to the level of pre-tax pay which the Review Body considers appropriate for GPs to earn, known as net remuneration, and the resulting figure becomes the gross remuneration. The various fees and allowances that comprise a GP's pay are then adjusted so that during the year they yield for the average GP the total gross and net remuneration which the Review Body has deemed appropriate.

This exercise is complex, and because the 'targets' set by the Review Body are not always met, any under- or over-payment is allowed for in subsequent years. As the Department of Health is apprised of how much has been paid to GPs after the end of a financial year, it is not difficult to compare the level of average gross pay received with the original target. Average net pay is more difficult to calculate because this depends upon an analysis of income tax returns.

Because GPs wish to obtain tax relief, they inform the Inland Revenue of the expenditure they have incurred in providing general medical services. This is a principal and vital source of information for estimating GP expenses. The Inland Revenue provides, annually, anonymized information relating to a sample of GPs' accounts. It includes all personal professional and partnership expenses.

General practitioner accounts

As the level of expenses to be reimbursed is always based upon samples of income tax returns, it is vital that every GP should show all the expenses incurred in providing general medical services in his or her accounts. GPs should enter the full amounts of both directly and indirectly reimbursed expenses, including those items that may not appear in cash books, bank statements or cheque books. Examples include those payments made by FHSAs directly to District Health Authorities (or other bodies) on behalf of the practice, and health centre rents, waste disposal charges and levies. The practice of 'netting off' expenses against matching income must be avoided; failure to include expenses, however small, reduces the funding available to the profession as a whole.

3 The General Practitioner's Terms of Service

THE GP working in the NHS has a contract with the FHSA to provide general medical services to his or her NHS patients. It is important to note that the contract is with the FHSA not the patient, in contrast to other countries where doctors have a direct contractual commitment to patients. Given this independent contractor status with a statutory authority within a publicly funded health service, it is not surprising to find that the NHS GP's contract has been enshrined in legislation, the NHS General Medical and Pharmaceutical Services Regulations (*see* Table 3.1).

The regulations, which include the GP's terms of service, provide the legal framework within which the business of NHS general practice is conducted. Because these regulations are laid down by Parliament they resemble an Act of Parliament; their legalistic style makes them difficult for the layman to comprehend, and this difficulty is compounded by the ever-growing number of amendments. The Regulations have been amended on several occasions; as many as a dozen amendments have been issued since 1 April 1985 following the introduction of the limited list of NHS drugs. However, in November 1989 major amendments were introduced to implement new contractual arrangements with effect from 1 April 1990, and each GP was sent a copy of the amended terms of service.

There is an understandable reluctance to provide a definitive explanatory guide to the Regulations. Since they carry the force of law, any dispute about their application or meaning can be resolved only by reference to the original text. Each copy of the Regulations, and subsequent amending Regulations, is accompanied by an official explanatory note, but it is always stated that this accompanying note does not form part of the Regulations as such. Nevertheless, a doctor needs to know what is required to fulfil the contract with the FHSA. In part, this knowledge is acquired from colleagues and partners, and from contacts with the FHSA. Advice from the General Medical Services Committee (GMSC) and from the Local Medical Committee (LMC), together with information in the medical journals, also help to familiarize the doctor with the Regulations and terms of service. Such advice should help a GP to be aware of current issues concerning interpretation and application.

Every GP should have access to a copy of the principal Regulations and each of the amending Regulations. Copies are distributed to GPs by FHSAs, and additional copies may be obtained from that source. However, because the amendments appear complicated and the format of the printed text of the original Regulations makes it difficult to incorporate handwritten

Table 3.1.   National Health Service (General Medical and Pharmaceutical Services) Regulations 1974, as amended

The Regulations are arranged in 11 parts:

I   General: definition of terms

II   Doctors: preparation of the medical list by the FHSA; child health surveillance and minor surgery lists; inclusion and removal of doctors on the list; local directory; withdrawals from the list

III   Medical Practices Committee: membership; reports from FHSAs; procedure for filling vacancies; certificate that transaction does not involve sale of goodwill

IV   Method of obtaining general medical services: describes how patients apply to be on a doctor's list; how patients are assigned to doctors; how limits are applied to the number of patients on a doctor's list; how patients may transfer to another doctor; the temporary arrangements for a practice where a doctor ceases to be on the medical list; the procedure for removing a patient from a doctor's list; arrangements for temporary residents

V   Method of obtaining maternity medical services

VI   Payments to doctors: requires the Secretary of State to publish the Statement of Fees and Allowances (the Red Book)

VII   Chemists

VIII   Provision of pharmaceutical services by doctors: describes the arrangements for doctors to supply drugs and appliances

VIIIA   Provides for the FHSA to establish a dispensing sub-committee and the determination of a controlled locality

VIIIB   Provides for the Rural Dispensing Committee to determine applications to provide pharmaceutical services and for appeals relating to the rurality of an area

IX   Various miscellaneous matters, including arrangements for claims and overpayments

amendments, few practices have an up-to-date amended set of the Regulations. A typical practice may have rarely referred to the Regulations and, if a difficulty ever arose, a GP would usually seek advice from the LMC secretary or the FHSA general manager.

Alleged breaches of the terms of service by a GP are normally dealt with by the Medical Service Committee (MSC) of the FHSA with which the GP is in contract. A separate set of Parliamentary Regulations deals with the MSC procedure: Statutory Instrument No 455 (1974), The National Health Service (Services Committees and Tribunal) Regulations 1974, and subsequent amendments.

It is essential that the Regulations are read and understood because they contain the terms of service which form the basis of the GP's contract with the NHS. It is vital that the GP refers to them if any problems arise, and if there is any doubt about their meaning a GP should seek advice from the LMC.

The commentary below focuses on the main aspects of the GP's terms of service. It should aid understanding of schedule 1 of the Regulations, which contains the GP's terms of service. This selective commentary is not, however, a substitute for the original text of the terms of service and should not therefore be quoted if any problem should arise.

The 1990 contract

The recent amendments to the Regulations have introduced into the GP's terms of service important elements of the contract such as would previously have been included in the Statement of Fees and Allowances (SFA or Red Book); namely those relating to the detailed arrangements for the provision of child health surveillance and minor surgery services, and the screening of elderly patients, newly registered patients and patients not seen within the last three years. By including these parts of the contract in the Regulations, rather than in the SFA, the Government can ensure that they are subject to Parliamentary rather than administrative control. By this means they are kept firmly in the public arena and are not able to be modified without the explicit consent of Parliament.

The terms of service for doctors (schedule 1, part 1 of the NHS (General Medical and Pharmaceutical Services) Regulations 1974, as amended)

Professional judgment

When a GP has to decide what, if any, professional action needs to be taken under the terms of service, in reaching a decision, he or she is not to be expected to exercise a higher degree of skill, knowledge and care than may reasonably be expected of GPs generally. Any GP who wants clarification on a matter involving professional judgement should consult his or her LMC secretary or medical defence body. The same general principle also applies to GPs providing child health surveillance or minor surgery services; in each area the level of skill, knowledge and care expected is that which may reasonably be expected of any doctor included in either list.

Patients

The terms of service list those categories of persons who are a GP's patients, (*see* Table 3.2). Most are self-evident. However, it is important to note that if a patient seeking treatment, claims to be on a GP's list but fails to produce a medical card, and the GP has reasonable doubts about the claim, the GP should provide treatment but is entitled to ask for a fee. If the patient is subsequently able to prove to the FHSA that he or she is on the GP's list, the fee has to be refunded.

Table 3.2.   Who are a GP's patients?

The main categories are:

1   Persons on the GP's list

2   Persons whom the GP has accepted or agreed to accept on his or her list, and who have not been notified to him or her by the FHSA as having ceased to be on his or her list

3   For a limited period of 14 days, persons the GP has refused to accept on to his or her list, if they live in the practice area and are not on the list of another doctor in the same area, or persons the GP has refused to accept as temporary residents

4   Persons who have been assigned to the GP under Regulation 16

5   For a limited period, persons about whom the GP has been notified that an application has been made for assignment to him or her

6   Persons accepted as temporary residents

7   Persons to whom the GP has agreed to provide child health surveillance services or minor surgery services

8   Persons to whom the GP is requested to give treatment which is immediately required owing to an accident or other emergency at any place in the practice area, or any persons to whom the GP agrees on request to give treatment which is immediately required owing to an accident or other emergency at any place in the FHSA locality, provided that there is no other doctor at the time otherwise available to give treatment

9   Persons for whom the GP is acting as a deputy to another doctor under the terms of service

10   Persons for whom the GP has been appointed as a deputy to treat temporarily

11   Women for whom the GP has undertaken to provide contraceptive or maternity medical services

Provision of child health surveillance and minor surgery

Any GP who is on the medical list may provide to a patient on his or her list (or on a partner's list or the list of a GP with whom he or she is in group practice) child health surveillance or minor surgery services, and may be paid for these services if included on the relevant list of the FHSA.

A GP who has agreed to provide child health surveillance services, should:

1 provide those services listed in Table 3.3 below (except for any examination the parent refuses to allow) until the child attains the age 5;
2 maintain the records specified in Table 3.4;
3 provide the health authority with the information specified in Table 3.5.

Table 3.3. Child health surveillance services

These services comprise:

(a) the monitoring:
   (i)   by the consideration of information concerning the child received by or on behalf of the doctor, and
   (ii) on any occasion when the child is examined or observed by or on behalf of the doctor (whether pursuant to sub-paragraph (b) or otherwise) of the health, well-being and physical, mental and social development (all of which characteristics are referred to as 'development') of the child while under the age of 5 years with a view to detecting any deviations from normal development;
(b) the examination of the child by or on behalf of the doctor on so many occasions and at such intervals as shall have been agreed between the FHSA and the health authority in whose district the child resides ('the relevant health authority') for the purpose of the provision of child health surveillance services generally in that district

Table 3.4. Child health surveillance services: Records

The GP should keep an accurate record of:

(a) the development of the child under the age of 5 years, compiled as soon as is reasonably practicable following the first examination and, where appropriate, amended following each subsequent examination; and
(b) the responses (if any) to offers made to the child's parent for the child to undergo any examination.

Table 3.5. Child health surveillance services

The GP should provide the health authority with the following information:

(a) a statement, to be prepared and dispatched to the relevant health authority as soon as is reasonably practicable following any examination, of the procedures undertaken in the course of that examination and of the doctor's findings in relation to each such procedure;
(b) such further information regarding the development of the child while under the age of 5 years as the relevant health authority may request.

A GP who has agreed to provide minor surgery services should:

1 offer to provide any of the procedures listed in Table 3.6 which are considered to be appropriate;
2 if providing minor surgery services to a patient not on his or her list, inform the patient's GP in writing of the outcome of the procedure.

Table 3.6. Minor surgery procedures

Injections	intra articular
	peri articular
	varicose veins
	haemorrhoid
Aspirations	joints
	cysts
	bursae
	hydrocele
Incisions	abcesses
	cysts
	thrombosed piles
Excisions	sebaceous cysts
	lipoma
	skin lesions for histology
	intradermal naevi, papilloma, dermatofibroma and similar conditions
	warts
	removal of toe nails (partial and complete)
Curette cautery and cryocautery	warts and verrucae
	other skin lesions (eg molluscum contagiosum)
Other	removal of foreign bodies
	nasal cautery

Termination of responsibility for patients

The GP may apply to the FHSA to have any person removed from his or her list. This takes effect on the date of acceptance by, or assignment to, another doctor, or on the eighth day after applying to the FHSA, whichever occurs sooner. However, if the GP is treating the person when removal would normally take effect, the FHSA should be informed and removal will then take effect only on the eighth day after the FHSA receives notification that the patient no longer requires treatment or upon acceptance by another doctor, whichever occurs first.

This right to remove a patient has to be set against the duty of an FHSA to assign a patient to a GP when the patient is unable to obtain acceptance voluntarily. In an area served by only one GP, this severely restricts a doctor's right to remove.

A GP may also stop providing maternity medical services to a woman by agreement with her, and failing this may apply for permission to terminate the agreement. The FHSA may agree to this after considering the views of either party, and after consulting the LMC. If the GP stops providing maternity medical services, the patient must be told so that she can make alternative arrangements with another doctor.

A GP's agreement to provide child health surveillance services may be terminated:

1 by either the parent or the doctor;
2 if the child has been removed from the doctor's list (or his or her partner's list or that of a doctor with whom he or she is associated in a group practice);
3 if the parent fails to respond to an invitation to arrange for the child to attend for examination within 42 days.

If the GP's undertaking to provide these services has ceased to be effective he or she should inform the FHSA and, where appropriate, inform the patient.

Service to patients

The GP is required to provide for his or her patients all necessary and appropriate personal medical services of the type usually provided by GPs. The doctor should do so at the practice premises or, if the condition of the patient so requires, elsewhere in the practice area or where the patient was living when accepted as a patient. The GP is not required to visit or treat the patient at any other place, but care has to be taken to ensure that neither the GP nor a member of his or her staff implies willingness to visit at an address outside the practice area. If this happens, the GP may be bound by a duty to visit.

These services include arrangements for referring patients to other NHS services, and advice to enable them to obtain help from the local authority social services department.

There is no obligation to provide contraceptive services, child health surveillance services, minor surgery services, or, except in an emergency, maternity services, unless the GP has previously agreed to do so.

The doctor should, unless prevented by an emergency, attend and treat any patient who comes for treatment at the places and during the hours approved by the FHSA, other than a patient who attends when an appointment system is in operation and who has not previously made an appointment. In these circumstances the doctor may decline to see the patient during that surgery period, providing the patient's health would not be put at risk and the patient is offered an appointment to attend within a reasonable time. The GP should take all reasonable steps to ensure that a consultation is not so deferred without his or her knowledge.

Recent amendments to the Regulations specify in detail the nature of certain of the services a GP is required to provide. These include:

1 giving advice, as appropriate, to a patient about the patient's general health, and in particular about diet, exercise, the use of tobacco, the consumption of alcohol and the misuse of drugs and solvents;
2 offering patients consultations and, where appropriate, physical examinations to identify or reduce the risk of disease or injury;
3 offering patients, as appropriate, vaccination or immunization against measles, mumps, rubella, pertussis, poliomyelitis, diphtheria and tetanus;
4 arranging for patients to be referred to other NHS services;
5 giving advice to enable patients to obtain help from a local authority social services department.

Newly registered patients

If a patient has been accepted on to a GP's list (or assigned to the list) the doctor should within 28 days offer the patient a consultation to:

1 obtain details of the patient's medical history, including that of his or her family, relating to:
   (i)   illnesses, immunizations, allergies, hereditary conditions, medication and tests carried out for breast or cervical cancer;
   (ii) social factors (including employment, housing and family circumstances) which may affect health;
   (iii) life-style factors (including diet, exercise, use of tobacco, consumption of alcohol, and misuse of drugs and solvents) which may affect health;
   (iv) the current state of the patient's health.
2 physically examine the patient:
   (i)   measuring height, weight and blood pressure;
   (ii) taking and analysing a urine sample to identify the presence of albumin and glucose.
3 record – in the patient's notes – the results of this examination;
4 assess whether and to what extent personal medical services should be provided to the patient;
5 offer to discuss with the patient (or the parent of a child patient) the conclusions of the consultation as to the state of the patient's health.

When a consultation for this purpose is offered, the GP should:

1 provide a *written* invitation – or if the initial invitation is made orally, provide written confirmation;
2 record in the patient's medical records the date of each invitation and whether or not it was accepted;
3 where, as a result of making the invitation, the doctor becomes aware that a patient is no longer residing at the address given in the records, inform the FHSA.

A GP is not required to offer a consultation to a newly registered patient:

1 if he or she is a restricted services principal (a principal who has only undertaken to provide general medical services limited to child health services, contraceptive services, maternity medical services, or minor surgery services, or any combination of these);
2 if the patient is a child under the age of 5;
3 if the patient was, immediately before joining his or her list, on the list of a partner and had already participated in a consultation of this kind during the previous 12 months.

If a GP assumes responsibility for a list of patients on succession to a vacant practice or otherwise becomes responsible for a sizeable number of new patients over a short period, the GP can ask the FHSA to defer the obligation to offer these consultations.

Patients not seen within 3 years

A GP is required to offer to each patient on his or her list a consultation to assess whether personal medical services are needed, if the patient:

1 is between the ages of 16 and 75 years;
2 has within the preceding 3 years attended neither a consultation with nor a clinic provided by any doctor in the course of the provision of general medical services;
3 has not been offered a consultation for this purpose within the previous 12 months.

During this consultation the GP should obtain the information listed in Table 3.7 and offer a physical examination including the procedures listed in Table 3.7.

The GP should record the findings and assess whether the patient requires treatment.

Patients aged 75 years and over

The GP should offer each patient a consultation and a domiciliary visit (which may be combined) to assess whether the patient requires treatment.

Table 3.7. Patients not seen within 3 years: information to be obtained and procedures to be undertaken during the consultation

Where appropriate the GP should obtain from the patient the following details of his or her medical history and, if relevant to the patient's medical history, that of his or her consanguineous family:

(i)   illnesses, immunizations, allergies, hereditary diseases, medication and tests carried out for breast or cervical cancer,
(ii) social factors (including employment, housing and family circumstances) which may affect health,
(iii) life-style factors (including diet, exercise, use of tobacco, consumption of alcohol, and misuse of drugs or solvents) which may affect health, and
(iv) the current state of the patient's health;

The GP should also offer to undertake a physical examination of the patient, comprising:

(i)   the measurement of blood pressure;
(ii) the taking of a urine sample and its analysis to identify the presence of albumin and glucose; and
(iii) the measurements necessary to detect any changes in body mass;

record, in the patient's medical records, the findings arising out of the details supplied by, and any examination of, the patient;

assess whether and, if so, in what manner and to what extent the GP should render personal medical services to the patient; and

in so far as it would not, in the opinion of the doctor, be likely to cause serious damage to the physical or mental health of the patient to do so, offer to discuss with the patient the conclusions the doctor has drawn as a result of the consultation as to the state of the patient's health.

This offer should be made no later than 1 April 1991 to any patient over the age of 75 years on the GP's list on 31 March 1990. For a patient who attains the age of 75 on or after 1 April 1990, the domiciliary visit and consultation should be offered within 12 months of the patient's 75th birthday. If a patient joins a GP's list after 1 April 1990 and is already aged 75, the offer should be made within 12 months of joining the list. The GP should make the invitation in writing (or confirm it in writing if it was initially made orally) and keep a record of the date of the invitation and whether it was accepted.

The doctor should record anything which appears to be affecting the patient's general health, including:

● sensory functions
● mobility
● mental condition
● physical condition including continence
● social environment
● use of medicines.

The GP should also record the findings of the domiciliary visit. After the domiciliary consultation, the GP should offer to discuss with the patient the conclusions that have been drawn.

Absences, deputies, assistants and partners

Normally, a GP should give treatment personally. However, in the case of general medical services other than maternity medical services (MMS), child health surveillance and minor surgery services, the GP is under no obligation to do so if reasonable steps are taken to ensure continuity of treatment by another doctor acting as a deputy, irrespective of whether the other doctor is a partner or an assistant. In addition, if it is reasonable to delegate the clinical treatment to a person whom the GP has authorized and who is competent to carry it out (for example a qualified nurse), the GP may do so.

A doctor on the obstetric list should not, without the FHSA's consent, employ to provide maternity services a deputy or assistant who is not, or is not qualified by experience to be, a doctor on the obstetric list. However, this does not apply in an obstetric emergency.

As for child health surveillance services, a GP who has agreed to provide these may employ a deputy or an assistant who is on a child health surveillance list, or with the FHSA's agreement another deputy or assistant. A GP who has agreed to provide minor surgery services may employ a deputy or assistant who is on a minor surgery list.

In general, a GP is responsible for the acts and omissions of any doctor acting as his or her deputy, whether the deputy is a partner or an assistant. A GP is similarly responsible for any person he or she employs or who is acting on his or her behalf. However, a GP is not responsible under the terms of service for the acts and omissions of a deputy who is on the list of the same FHSA.

The FHSA should be informed of any standing deputizing arrangements unless the deputy is the GP's assistant or is already on the FHSA's list, and carries out these arrangements at the premises where the doctor normally practises. If a GP intends to be absent for more than a week, the FHSA should be informed of the doctor or doctors responsible for the practice during the period of absence.

Before entering into any arrangement with a deputizing service, a GP should obtain the FHSA's consent. When giving its consent, the FHSA may impose conditions to ensure the adequacy of these arrangements. However, before refusing consent or imposing conditions, the FHSA must consult the LMC. The FHSA is required to review any consent given or conditions imposed in consultation with the LMC, and may withdraw consent or alter the conditions. A GP may appeal to the Secretary of State against a refusal of consent or the imposition of conditions, or against the withdrawal of consent or a variation of the conditions.

The GP should taken reasonable steps to satisfy him- or herself that a doctor whom he or she intends to employ as a deputy or assistant is not disqualified for inclusion on the FHSA's medical list or has not given an undertaking that he or she will not apply for admission to a medical list of an FHSA. Nor should a GP (without the consent of the Secretary of State) employ a doctor who is so disqualified or who has given such an undertaking. The GP should inform the FHSA of the name of any assistant employed and of when this employment ends. A doctor should not employ one or more assistants for more than 3 months in a period of 12 months without the FHSA's consent. The FHSA may review and withdraw its consent, but, before refusing or withdrawing consent, the FHSA must consult the LMC. (A GP may appeal to the Medical Practices Committee (MPC) against refusal or withdrawal of consent.) If consent is withdrawn, the decision will not take effect for a month; but if an appeal is made to the MPC against the withdrawal and the MPC dismisses the appeal, the withdrawal takes effect from a date determined by the MPC, which must be not less than 1 month after the date of the dismissal of the appeal. (A doctor acting as a deputy can treat patients at places and times other than those arranged by the GP for whom he or she is acting although regard must be given to the convenience of the patients.)

Arrangements at practice premises

The GP should provide adequate accommodation at the practice premises 'having regard to the circumstances of his practice' and is required, on receiving a written request from the FHSA, to allow the premises to be visited at any reasonable time by a representative of the FHSA, or the LMC, or both.

If the GP intends to operate an appointment system, or succeeds to or joins a practice where this is already running, the FHSA should be notified of any appointment system he or she proposes to operate or of any proposal to discontinue this system.

With certain important exceptions, a GP should not, without the consent of the FHSA (or, on appeal, the MPC), practise at premises that have been previously used for practice purposes by another doctor whose practice has been declared vacant and to whose practice a successor has been or is to be appointed.

The GP should not without the consent of the FHSA (or, on appeal, the MPC) start to practise in any premises within 1 year of their having ceased to be occupied or used for the purpose of practice by another doctor who within 1 month of such cessation begins practising at a group practice premises, as a member of a group, or at a health centre less than 3 miles away from the original premises. (This does not apply if the former occupant gives written consent for another doctor to use the premises.)

Employees

Before employing any member of staff, the GP should ensure that the person is suitably qualified and competent to carry out the required duties. In particular, the doctor should take account of the employee's academic and vocational qualifications, training and previous experience. The GP should also offer the employee reasonable training opportunities.

Doctors' availability to patients

Any GP should normally be available at times and places approved by the FHSA and inform patients of his or her availability. In general, the FHSA will not approve any application unless it is satisfied that the times proposed by the GP are such that he or she is normally available:

1 42 weeks in any period of 12 months
2 during not less than 26 hours in any such week
3 on 5 days in any such week
4 with hours of availability which are likely to be convenient to patients.

There are important exceptions to this basic requirement.

1 A GP may seek to be normally available for 26 hours over a 4 day week, if he is involved in health related activities other than the provision of general medical services to his or her patients (*see* Table 3.8 overleaf, for a broad definition of health related activities). But the four day availability will not be approved by the FHSA if it considers that the effectiveness of the doctor's services to patients is likely to be significantly reduced or patients are likely to suffer significant inconvenience.
2 A GP may seek to be available for less than 26 hours a week, if practising in a partnership. In this case there are two options:
  (i)   less than 26 hours but not less than 19 hours;
  (ii) less than 19 hours but not less than 13 hours.
3 Two doctors may apply for FHSA approval to be jointly available for 26 hours a week, if they are in partnership.

Practice area

A doctor may not open premises in any area or part of the area of an FHSA where, at the time of the application, the MPC considers that the number of practitioners providing general medical services is already adequate. Subject to this condition, a GP may at any time apply to the FHSA for consent to alter the extent of his or her practice area. (If the FHSA refuses consent, the GP may appeal to the Secretary of State.)

Table 3.8.   List of health-related activities

1 activities connected with the organization of the medical profession or the training of its members
2 activities connected with the provision of medical care or treatment
3 activities connected with the improvement of the quality of such care or treatment
4 activities connected with the administration of general medical services
5 appointments concerning medical education or training
6 medical appointments within the health service other than in relation to the provision of general medical services
7 medical appointments under the Crown, with Government Departments or Agencies, or public or local authorities
8 appointments concerning the regulation of the medical profession or service on the Medical Practices Committee

Notification of change of place of residence

When a GP changes his or her place of residence, the FHSA should be notified in writing within 28 days.

Records

A GP should keep adequate records of the illnesses and treatment of patients on forms supplied by the FHSA, and should send these records to the FHSA on request as soon as possible. Within 14 days of being informed by the FHSA of a patient's death (or not later than one month after otherwise learning of it), a GP should return the records to the FHSA.

Certification

A GP should issue to patients or their personal representatives free of charge the certificates listed in Table 3.9 if they are reasonably required. However, a GP is not obliged to do so if the patient is being attended by another doctor (other than a partner, assistant or deputy) or is not being treated by, or under the supervision of, a doctor. In certain circumstances, a GP may issue a statement, without an examination, advising the patient to refrain from work for a period of up to a month, provided a written report, not more than a month old, has been received from another doctor at a hospital, place of employment or other institution. The other doctor should not be a partner, assistant or deputy.

Table 3.9. List of prescribed medical certificates

Medical certificate	Short title of enactment under or for the purpose of which certificate required
1. To support a claim to obtain either personally or by proxy under the enactments specified	Child Benefit Act 1975 (c.61)
	Parts I and III of the Social Security and Housing Benefits Act 1982 (1982 c.24)
	Social Security Act 1975 (c. 14)
	Supplementary Benefits Act 1976 (c.71)
	Industrial Injuries and Diseases (Old Cases) Act 1975 (c.16)
2. To prove inability to work or incapacity for self-support for the purposes of an award by the Secretary of State for Social Services	Pensions (Navy, Army, Air Force and Mercantile Marine) Act 1939 (2 & 3 Geo, 6c.83)
	Parts I and III of the Social Security and Housing Benefits Act 1982 (1982 c.24)
	Pensions Act (Mercantile Marine) 1942 (5 & 6 Geo. 6c.26)
3. To enable proxy to draw pensions, etc.	Naval and Marine Pay and Pensions Act 1965 (28 & 29 Vict. c.73)
	Air Force (Constitution) Act 1917 (7 & 8 Geo. 5c.51)
	Personal Injuries (Emergency Provisions) Act 1939 (2 & 3 Geo. 6c.82)
	Polish Resettlement Act 1947 (10 & 11 Geo. 6c.19)
	Home Guard Act 1951 (15 & 16 Geo., 6 and 1 Eliz.2.c.8) S.I. 1982/1983 Parts I and III of the Social Security and Housing Benefits Act 1982 (1982 c.24) S.I. 1987 No 407
	Part V of, and Schedule 4 to, the Social Security Act 1986 (1986 c.50)
4. To establish pregnancy for the purpose of obtaining welfare foods	Emergency Laws (Re-enactments and Repeals) Act 1964 (1964 c.60)
5. To enable patient to have his sight test under the General Ophthalmic Services	National Health Service Act 1977 (c.49)
6. To establish fitness to receive inhalational analgesia in childbirth	Midwives Act 1951 (14 & 15 Geo. 6c.53).
7. To secure registration of stillbirth	Births and Deaths Registration Act 1953 (1 & 2 Eliz. 2c.20)
8. To enable payment to be made to an institution or other person in case of mental disorder of persons entitled to payment from public funds	Section 142 of the Mental Health Act 1983 (Eliz. 2c.20 c.72)

Table 3.9. Continued

Medical certificate	Short title of enactment under or for the purpose of which certificate required
9. To establish unfitness for jury service	S.10 Juries Act 1974 (1974 c.23)
10. To establish unfitness to attend for medical examinations	National Service Act 1948 (11 & 12 Geo. 6c.64)
11. To support late application for reinstatement in civil employment or notification of non-availability to take up employment, owing to sickness	Reinstatement in Civil Employment Act 1944 (7 & 8 Geo. 6c.15)
	Reinstatement in Civil Employment Act 1950 (14 & 15 Geo. 6c.10)
	Reserve and Auxiliary Forces (Training) Act 1951 (14 & 15 Geo. 6c.23)
	Army Reserve Act 1962 (10 & 11 Eliz. 2c.10)
	Ulster Defence Regiment Act 1969 (1969 c.65)
12. To enable a person to be registered as an absent voter on grounds of physical incapacity	Representation of the People Act 1983 (Eliz 2c.2)
13. To support application for certificates conferring exemption from charges in respect of drugs, medicines and appliances	National Health Service Act 1977 (c.49)
14. To support a claim by or on behalf of a severely mentally impaired person for exemption from liability to pay the personal community charge	Local Government Finance Act 1988 (c.41)

Acceptance of fees

A GP must not demand or accept a fee or other remuneration for any treatment, including maternity medical services, whether under the terms of service or not, given to a person for whose treatment he or she is responsible. A doctor must take all practical steps to ensure that his or her partner, deputy, or assistant does not demand or accept any remuneration for treatment given to his or her patients unless, of course, the partner, deputy or assistant would have been entitled to charge if the patient had been on his or her own list.

There are, however, certain specific circumstances in which a GP may accept a fee. These are listed in Table 3.10.

There are other certificates and reports which are not part of a GP's NHS obligations to patients. The fee for these is a matter to be agreed between the GP and the patient. The BMA issues agreed and recommended lists of fees for these procedures.

Table 3.10.   Specific circumstances in which a GP may accept a fee

(a) from any statutory body for services rendered for the purpose of that body's statutory functions

(b) from any body, employer or school for a routine medical examination of persons for whose welfare the body, employer or school is responsible, or an examination of such persons for the purpose of advising the body, employer or school of any administrative action they might take

(c) for treatment which is not of a type usually provided by general practitioners and which is given:

   (i)   pursuant to the provisions of Sections 1 and 2 of the Health Services and Public Health Act 1968(a), or

   (ii) in a registered nursing home which is not providing services under the Health Services Acts,

   if (in either case) the doctor is serving on the staff of a hospital providing services under the Health Service Acts as a specialist providing treatment of the kind the patient requires and if within 7 days from giving the treatment the doctor supplies the FHSA, on a form provided by it for the purpose, with such information about the treatment as it may require

(d) under Section 155 of the Road Traffic Act 1972

(e) from a dentist in respect of the provision at his request of anaesthetic for a person for whom the dentist is providing general dental services

(f) when a doctor treats a patient under paragraph 4(2), in which case the doctor shall be entitled to demand and accept a reasonable fee (recoverable under paragraph 33) for any treatment given and for any drugs and appliances supplied, if he gives the patient a receipt on a form supplied by the FHSA

   Paragraph (g) deleted by S.I. 1975 No. 719 but other paragraphs have not been changed

(h) for attending and examining (but not otherwise treating) a patient at his request at a police station in connection with proceedings which the police are minded to bring against him

(i) for treatment consisting of an immunization for which no remuneration is payable by the FHSA in pursuance of the Statement made under regulation 24 and which is requested in connection with travel abroad

(j) for circumcising a patient for whom such an operation is requested on religious grounds and is not needed on any medical ground

(k) for prescribing or supplying medicine for a patient who requires to have it in his possession solely in anticipation of the onset of an ailment while he is outside the United Kingdom but for which he is not requiring treatment when the medicine is prescribed or supplied

(l) for a medical examination to enable a decision to be made whether or not it is inadvisable on medical grounds for a person to wear a seat belt

(m) where the person is not one to whom any of paragraphs (a), (b) or (c) of section 38 (1) of the NHS Act 1977 (a) applies (including by reason of regulations under section 38 (6) of that Act), for testing the sight of that person

Table 3.11.   Information to be included in practice leaflets

Personal and professional details of the doctor

1 full name
2 sex
3 medical qualifications registered by the General Medical Council
4 date and place of first registration as medical practitioner

Practice information

5 the times approved by the FHSA during which the doctor is personally available for consultation by his patients at his practice premises
6 whether an appointments system is operated by the doctor for consultations at his practice premises
7 if there is an appointments system, the method of obtaining a non-urgent appointment and the method of obtaining an urgent appointment
8 the method of obtaining a non-urgent domiciliary visit and the method of obtaining an urgent domiciliary visit
9 the doctor's arrangements for providing personal medical services when he is not personally available
10 the method by which patients are to obtain repeat prescriptions from the doctor
11 if the doctor's practice is a dispensing practice, the arrangements for dispensing prescriptions
12 if the doctor provides clinics for his patients, their frequency, duration and purpose
13 the numbers of staff, other than doctors, assisting the doctor in his practice, and a description of their roles
14 whether the doctor provides (1) maternity medical services (2) contraceptive services (3) child health surveillance services (4) minor surgery services
15 whether the doctor works single-handed, in partnership, part-time or on a job share basis, or within a group practice
16 the nature of any arrangements whereby the doctor or his staff receive patients' comments on his provision of general medical services
17 the geographical boundary of his practice area by reference to a sketch, diagram or plan of a scale approved by the FHSA
18 whether the doctor's practice premises have suitable access for all disabled patients and, if not the reasons why they are unsuitable for particular types of disability
19 if an assistant is employed, details for him as specified in paragraph 1–4 of this Schedule
20 if the practice either is a general practitioner training practice for the purposes of the National Health Service (Vocational Training) Regulations 1979 (a) or undertakes the teaching of undergraduate medical students, the nature of arrangements for drawing this to the attention of patients

A doctor must not demand or accept a fee or other remuneration from a patient for prescribing or supplying any drug or chemical reagent or appliance, unless the patient requires to have a medicine solely in antici-pation of the onset of an ailment outside the United Kingdom but for which he or she is not requiring treatment when the medicine is prescribed or supplied.

Prescribing and dispensing

A GP is required to supply drugs or listed appliances needed for immediate treatment of a patient before a supply can be obtained elsewhere. In the course of treating a patient under general medical services, a GP must not issue a prescription for a drug or other substance listed in schedule 3A to the Regulations (the 'black list') for supply under the NHS, and if the GP is not entitled to dispense he or she must not supply any such drug. In the case of a drug listed under schedule 3B, a doctor may prescribe and supply only in certain circumstances. A GP may prescribe these items privately, but may not charge for doing so. The GP can only charge for the item itself if he or she is already entitled to dispense to a patient and the GP can only do so for a particular course of treatment.

Practice leaflets

A GP should prepare a practice leaflet including the information in Table 3.11 on page 27.

The leaflet should be reviewed at least annually and amended to maintain accuracy. An up-to-date copy of this leaflet should be made available to the FHSA, to each patient on the doctor's list and to anyone who reasonably requires one. Leaflets may, of course, be prepared for partnerships.

Inquiries about prescriptions and referrals

The GP should be prepared to answer any inquiries from the FHSA relating to:

1   any prescriptions issued;
2   referrals to other NHS services.

Annual reports

A GP should provide the FHSA annually with a report containing the information in Table 3.12. Each report should be compiled for a 12 month period ending 31 March and should be sent to the FHSA by 30 June. The first annual report is due by 30 June 1991 and should refer to the year ending 31 March 1991. A partnership can, of course, produce a single report.

Conclusions

This commentary is selective, not comprehensive. Not all of the paragraphs in the terms of service have been covered and only a brief summary has been provided. If any problem should arise, a GP should refer to the Regulations and if necessary seek the advice and assistance of the LMC secretary or BMA regional office.

Table 3.12.   Information to be provided in annual reports

1 The number of staff, other than doctors, assisting the doctor in his practice by reference to:

    (i)   the total number but not by reference to their names;

    (ii) the principal duties of each employee and the hours each week the employee assists the doctor;

    (iii) the qualifications of each employee;

    (iv) the relevant training undertaken by each employee during the preceding 5 years.

2 The following information as respects the practice premises:

    (i)   any variations in relation to floor space, design or quality since the last annual report;

    (ii) any such variations anticipated in the course of the forthcoming period of 12 months.

3 The following information as respects the referral of patients to other services under the National Health Service Act 1977 during the period of the report:

(a) as respects those by the doctor to a specialist:

    (i)   the total number of patients referred as in-patients;

    (ii) the total number of patients referred as out-patients;

by reference in each case to whichever of the following clinical specialties applies and specifying in each case the name of the hospital concerned:

- General surgical
- General medical
- Orthopaedic
- Rheumatology (physical medicine)
- Ear, nose and throat
- Gynaecology
- Obstetrics
- Paediatrics
- Ophthalmology
- Psychiatry
- Geriatrics
- Dermatology
- Neurology
- Genitourinary
- X-ray
- Pathology
- Others (including plastic surgery, accident and emergency, endocrinology);

(b) the total number of cases of which the doctor is aware (by reference to the categories listed in sub-paragraph (a)) in which a patient referred himself to services under the National Health Service Act 1977.

Continued overleaf

Table 3.12. Continued

4 The doctor's other commitments as a medical practitioner with reference to:
    (i)   a description of any posts held; and
    (ii) a description of all work undertaken
including, in each case, the annual hourly commitment.

5 The nature of any arrangements whereby the doctor or his staff receive patients' comments on his provision of general medical services.

6 The following information as respects orders for drugs and appliances:
    (a) whether the doctor's practice has its own formulary;
    (b) whether the doctor uses a separate formulary;
    (c) the doctor's arrangements for the issue of repeat prescriptions to patients.

4 Basic Practice Allowance

Principals and assistants

Is the status of a salaried partner the same as that of a salaried assistant? What is the difference between a principal and an associate? Many GPs cannot answer these questions correctly, yet ignorance of their own status and that of their colleagues can expose them to enormous risks.

Some definitions are provided in the Red Book, and FHSAs will use these to establish whether a doctor should receive payments, and if so, which ones.

The most important distinction is between principals and those other doctors working in general practice who are not principals.

A *principal* is a practitioner who enters into a contract with an FHSA, as a single-handed practitioner, a single-handed practitioner but within a group, or a partner in a partnership. Under this contract, a principal accepts certain responsibilities defined in the terms of service, including responsibility for any doctors or staff he or she employs. A principal can apply for most of the payments described in the Red Book. A principal is self-employed, and if in a partnership participates in partnership decisions and is free to accept patients onto his or her list.

The main types of principal recognized as such by FHSAs are listed in Box 4.1.

Box 4.1: Types of principal

1 Full-time practitioner: an unrestricted principal providing general medical services for at least 26 hours a week
2 Three-quarter time practitioner: an unrestricted principal providing general medical services for at least 19 hours a week
3 Half-time practitioner: an unrestricted principal providing general medical services for at least 13 hours a week
4 Job sharer: an unrestricted principal who provides general medical services for at least 26 hours a week jointly with another unrestricted principal

---

A *salaried partner* is a partner who draws a share of the profits in the form of a salary. This arrangement may be challenged by the FHSA if it insists that all partners must declare their share of partnership profits as a fraction or a percentage of the total, not as a salary.

Unless a principal works single-handed (whether or not within a group) the FHSA must be satisfied that he or she is truly a partner. The NHS (General Medical and Pharmaceutical Services) Regulations 1974 (as amended) state that to be recognized as a partner, a full-time practitioner must receive a share of the partnership profits which is at least one-third of the share of the partnership profits enjoyed by the partner with the largest share.

This means that in a two doctor partnership the maximum variation between the shares of the senior and junior partner is three-quarters to one-quarter (one-quarter is at least one-third of three-quarters).

The Regulations also state that a three-quarter time partner must receive a share of the profits which is at least one-quarter of the profits enjoyed by the partner with the greatest share. A half- time practitioner must receive at least one-fifth of the share of the greatest sharing partner.

The 1990 contract recognizes part-time practitioners and job sharers officially for the first time.

Doctors who are not principals

The following are not recognized as principals; they do not have a contract with the FHSA and are not eligible to claim payments from the FHSA (with the exception of certain specific reimbursements).

Associate: a practitioner employed by a single-handed isolated practitioner with the agreement of the FHSA or Health Board.

Assistant: a practitioner employed by a principal with the consent of the FHSA, or a practitioner working within a partnership who is not a partner.

Trainee practitioner: a fully registered practitioner who is training in general practice and employed by an approved trainer. Trainers and trainees can claim certain reimbursements from the FHSA relating to the traineeship.

Locum: a doctor employed by a practitioner to assist him or her on a temporary or occasional basis.

It is vital that a practitioner establishes his or her status before accepting an appointment in general practice.

Box 4.2:

Principals have a contract with an FHSA and receive a wide range of payments described in the Red Book

Principals in a partnership must receive certain minimum shares of the profits

Principals are responsible for the acts and omissions of doctors they employ, e.g. associates, assistants, trainees and locums

---

Basic Practice Allowance

The Basic Practice Allowance (BPA) is the foundation stone of a GP's income for providing NHS general medical services. Other allowances depend on entitlement to the BPA. A GP should establish his or her entitlement to a full or partial BPA before applying to join an FHSA list. No BPA will be paid to a practitioner working within a partnership who is not deemed to be a partner. The BPA is a payment which recognizes the continuing responsibility and basic expenditure involved in providing general medical services during a normal working week. It reflects those standing expenses or overheads (apart from premises and staff) which do not vary proportionately with the list size.

Under the new contractual arrangements the conditions for payments of the BPA have been changed significantly. Eligibility now relates almost solely to list size and there is no requirement to devote a substantial amount of time to general practice (the previous so called '20 hour rule'). Requirements for availability are now included in the terms of service (e.g. the requirement that a full time GP should be available for at least 26 hours a week).

A full-time practitioner will be eligible for a full BPA if he or she provides general medical serices and has 1200 or more patients on his or her personal list, or is in a partnership with an average list of at least 1200 patients.

Under the old contract the list size requirement for payment of the full BPA was a list of 1000 patients.

A practitioner will be eligible for a lower rate of the BPA if he or she has at least 400 but no more than 1199 patients on his or her personal list, or is in a partnership with an average list within this range. Payment will be a lump sum for the first 400 patients plus additional amounts at different rates for each patient up to 600 patients, 800 patients, 1000 patients and 1200 patients.

Job sharers

Job sharers will be jointly eligible for a single BPA at the appropriate rate, determined by their combined list size (irrespective of their personal list sizes), or the average list size if they are members of a partnership.

Part-time practitioners

A part-time practitioner will be eligible for a BPA, but:

1 a part-time practitioner will only be eligible for one BPA; and

2 no half-time practitioner may earn an amount of BPA greater than that which would be payable for a list of 600 patients and no three-quarter time practitioner may earn an amount of BPA greater than that which would be payable for a list of 900 patients.

Calculating partnership average list size

In calculating a partnership average list size the FHSA will add together the personal list sizes of all the partners and divide this total figure by a common divisor which takes into account any fractions worked by part-time practitioners. Each partner will then be credited with the average number of patients multiplied by the appropriate figure reflecting the partner's time commitment, subject to the limitations on BPA for part-time practitioners specified above. For example, in a partnership of three full-time GPs and one half-time GP, the divisor will be 7 ($7 \times 0.50 = 3 + 0.50$), while in a partnership of two full-time GPs, one three-quarter time GP and one half-time GP, the divisor will be 13 ($13 \times 0.25 = 2 + 0.75 + 0.50$).

Box 4.3: Full BPA: eligibility requirements

1 A practitioner must provide general medical services
2 A practitioner must have at least 1200 patients on his or her personal list, or be in a partnership with such an average list

---

Leave payment

Part of the BPA expected to be paid during a financial year can be drawn in advance as a 'leave payment' when a holiday or period of study leave is taken. Applications for leave payment must be made on the FHSA's form by 15 April in the financial year during which leave is to be taken. Leave payments cannot be drawn for leave periods of less than a week.

Box 4.4: Leave payment

A leave payment is a part-payment of the BPA in advance

Applications must be made 15 April

Total leave payment cannot exceed one-fifth of the BPA

The total amount drawn cannot exceed on-fifth of the BPA, and is subsequently recovered through quarterly deductions spread across the financial year. Thus, a leave payment taken in May must be applied for by 15 April, and will be fully recovered by the following 31 March.

Leave payments are a useful way of improving a practice's cash flow.

5 Additions to the Basic Practice Allowance

THERE are several allowances for which a GP can only qualify if in receipt of a BPA.

The additions are for:

1 practice in a designated area
2 seniority
3 employment of an assistant.

The group practice allowance, special incentive for group practice and vocational training allowance been abolished with effect from 1 April 1990 under the 1990 contract.

The full amount of these additions will only be paid to a practitioner receiving the full BPA.

The amount of any addition payable to a GP who is not eligible for a full BPA is calculated as follows:

$$\frac{\text{the amount of BPA received}}{\text{the maximum rate of BPA}} \times \text{the appropriate addition}$$

Addition for practice in certain designated areas

Designated areas are those defined as under-doctored by the Medical Practices Committee after consulting the FHSA. Currently there are no designated areas and therefore no new payments will be made for this purpose. A few GPs are still receiving payments for practising in areas previously classified as designated, but their number is falling rapidly.

Payment of a Type 1 Allowance was made to GPs whose main surgery was in a locality that had been continuously designated as under-doctored for at least 3 years. Payment was made whilst the area remained designated or for a concessionary period of a further 3 years after this designation ceased. A Type 2 Allowance was paid to doctors whose main surgery was in an area continuously designated as under-doctored for 1 year with average lists of over 3000 patients. The payment was made for a concessionary period of 2 years after the average list size fell below 3000.

Because designated areas have disappeared (because average lists have dropped), GPs receiving this allowance have entered the concessionary payment periods, many of which have now finished. It is unlikely, but not inconceivable, that areas might in the future be categorized as designated. The FHSA will have details of such areas.

Box 5.1: Addition for practice in a designated area
Currently, no areas are classified as designated

Addition for seniority

An allowance is paid to a GP who has completed the prescribed years of registration with the General Medical Council (GMC) and of service as an unrestricted NHS GP. The three levels of seniority allowance are each related to the number of years' registration and service.

If the qualifying conditions are met and the GP is receiving a full BPA, he or she will receive the appropriate level of seniority payment in full. Proportionate payments are made to GPs receiving only part of the BPA. Job sharers are assessed for seniority payments on an individual basis and these are reduced pro rata according to the doctor's availability as notified to the FHSA.

Conditions for these payments are as follows; in each case the service quoted (whether in the NHS or HM Forces) must have been undertaken since 5 July 1948, when the NHS started.

1 First level: a GP registered with the GMC for 11 years or more who has been a principal providing unrestricted NHS general medical services or medical service in HM Forces recognized by the Secretary of State for an aggregate of at least 7 years.
2 Second level: registration for 18 years or more, and an aggregate of at least 14 years' service as an NHS principal or in a recognized post in HM forces.
3 Third level: registration for 25 years or more, and an aggregate of at least 21 years' service as an NHS principal or in a recognized post in HM Forces.

The provisions in Boxes 5.2 and 5.3 apply when working out the length of time a GP has been registered, and has been providing unrestricted NHS general medical services.

Box 5.2: Calculating number of years of registration

1 Registration by the GMC or the Medical Registration Council of the Republic of Ireland counts from the date of provisional (but not temporary or limited) registration if this date is shown, and otherwise from the date of full registration
2 The FHSA may allow a GP to count registration from the date of first registration by an overseas authority if the qualification is recognized by the GMC for provisional, full, temporary or limited registration
3 Registration must normally be continuous. Breaks in registration may affect the GP's right to receive seniority payments

Box 5.3: Calculating length of NHS general medical services provision

1 Service as an unrestricted NHS GP since 1948 counts, and absences because of compulsory national service, holiday, sick leave, study leave or a hospital attachment are ignored if the GP's name remained on the medical list
2 If a GP resigns from the medical list and returns to general practice after more than six months, there is a qualifying period before the GP is entitled to a seniority payment. The qualifying periods vary according to the length of the break. A break of between 6 and 18 months requires a qualifying period of 6 months, while a break of more than 90 months requires a qualifying period of 48 months. Service as an assistant, locum or principal during a break may be taken into account in assessing the length of break. Service in HM Forces in a recognized post is not regarded as a break. Service under Regulation 19(9) and 19(6)(temporary arrangements for conducting a practice) is taken into account
3 Claims for service as a medical officer in HM Forces to be recognized for seniority purposes have to be made to the FHSA.

Box 5.4: Addition for seniority: three levels of seniority payment

First: registered with GMC for 11 years or more
           principal GP for at least 7 years
Second: registered with GMC for 18 years or more
           principal GP for at least 14 years
Third: registered with GMC for 25 years or more
           principal GP for at least 21 years

Seniority payments normally continue to the age of 70 years, but payments may be made until the age of 72 years if the GP's continuing ability to provide general medical services is demonstrated to the FHSA in the light of advice from the LMC. Application has to be made just before the GP reaches 70 years of age, and again just before the age of 71 years. But, from 1 April 1991, compulsory retirement at the age of 70 years will be introduced.

Addition for the employment of an assistant

An allowance for employing a *full-time assistant* is paid to:

1 a single-handed full-time GP (or two job sharers) with a list of at least 3000 patients; or
2 a partnership of full-time GPs (including job sharers) with a minimum combined list of 3000 patients for the first full-time practitioner (or two job sharers) plus an average of 2500 patients for each other full-time practitioner (or set of two job sharers); or
3 a partnership of at least one full-time GP (or two job sharers) plus one or more part-time practitioners with a minimum combined list of 3000 patients for the first full-time practitioner (or two job sharers), 2500 patients for each other full-time practitioner (or set of two job sharers), 1875 patients for each three-quarter-time practitioner and 1250 patients for each half-time practitioner.

If the assistant is employed only part-time on NHS general medical services, the full allowance will be reduced.

An addition of half the appropriate rate will be paid for employing *an assistant working half-time or more* to:

1 a single-handed full-time practitioner (or two job sharers) with a list size of least 2500 patients; or
2 a partnership of full-time practitioners (including job sharers), with a minimum combined list of 2500 patients for the first full-time practitioner (or two job sharers) plus an average of 2250 patients for each other full-time practitioner (or set of two job sharers); or
3 a partnership of at least one full-time practitioner (or two job sharers) plus one or more part-time practitioners with a minimum combined list of 2500 patients for the first full-time practitioner (or set of two job sharers), 2250 patients for each other full-time practitioner (or job sharers), 1687 patients for each three-quarter practitioner and 1125 patients for each half-time practitioner.

Again the allowance is reduced if the assistant is employed less than half-time on NHS general medical services.

The list size requirements for a half-time assistant's allowance are relaxed for single-handed doctors, job sharers and partnerships which are receiving substantial rural practice payments.

Box 5.5: Addition for an assistant

1 Single-handed practitioners, job sharers and partnerships are eligible, depending on list size
2 List size requirement is reduced where only half-time allowance is claimed
3 List size requirement is also reduced if the GP or GPs are receiving substantial rural practice payments and are claiming only a half-time assistant's allowance

---

Eligibility for this allowance depends on partnership average list size, not individual list size. Only one allowance can be paid for each assistant employed.

All list size requirements are subject to a tolerance of 100 for full-time, 75 for three-quarter-time and 50 for half-time practitioners. Those who qualify initially for the allowance will not lose it until the beginning of the quarter after the list has fallen by at least the amount of the tolerance below the lower list size limit.

Claims for an assistant's allowance should be made on form FP80.

There are very few assistants employed in general practice for whom this allowance is claimed. This is because it has always been set at a level which made it insignificant compared to the allowances paid for a partner. Partnership is the preferred option for practices which are able to gain the permission of the FHSA and Medical Practices Committee for the appointment of an additional principal. Whether this preference continues will depend on doctors' assessment of the monetary value of the assistant's allowance under the 1990 contract compared to the allowances paid to a principal. Since this ratio has changed significantly in favour of the employment of an assistant, a substantial increase in the number of assistants employed may occur.

6 Associate Allowance

THE Associate Allowance allows single-handed isolated practitioners jointly to employ an associate doctor, so as to allow them time off for leisure and training, in circumstances where continuous duty is otherwise an intrinsic feature of general medical services.

Wherever possible, participating practitioners should ensure that associates have the opportunity to work in a single locality. In most cases there will be one associate doctor employed jointly between two adjacent practices, although the FHSA or Health Board may agree to an associate being employed between three practitioners in certain circumstances.

An associate must undertake the normal range of general medical services provided by the principal who employs him or her; the principal is responsible under the terms of service for all acts and omissions of the associate.

Practitioners who employ an assistant are not eligible to participate in this scheme.

To be eligible a single-handed GP (or job sharers) must be:

1 in receipt of rural practice payments; or
2 the sole practitioners on an island; and either
3 receiving an inducement payment; or
4 more than 10 miles by the most practicable route from the nearest practitioner's main surgery and the nearest District General Hospital.

Very few GPs in England will qualify for this new allowance.

Box 6.1: Associate Allowance: eligibility requirements

A single-handed practitioner (or job sharers) must be
1 in receipt of rural practice payments or
2 the sole practitioners on an island and
3 receiving an inducement payment or
4 in a practice 10 miles from the nearest practitioner's main surgery and nearest District General Hospital

---

Associate doctor

The associate must:

1 satisfy the requirements of the NHS (Vocational Training) Regulations 1979; and

2 not be on any FHSA or Health Board medical list whilst an associate; and
3 have a full-time commitment to general medical services duties between the two or more employing practitioners; and
4 be under 70.

Application to the FHSA for approval

Application for approval of the employment of an associate and to claim the allowance must be made on form FP/AA.

A copy of the associate's contract of employment must be provided, together with details of the arrangements for sharing the associate's time between the employing GPs. The form will also ask which employing GP is responsible for administering the contract of the associate and is to be paid the allowance by the FHSA or Health Board.

The employment of an associate disbars those GPs receiving inducement payments from claiming reimbursement of locum fees and expenses, other than in exceptional circumstances.

Under this scheme the employing practitioner is responsible for paying the associate and making deductions for national insurance and income tax. An associate may join the NHS superannuation scheme.

The employing practitioners may decide what rate of pay to give the associate but the FHSA or Health Board will pay an allowance at a rate specified in schedule 1 to the Red Book, which allows for incremental progression. It will also reimburse an allowance for the associate's use of a car.

An associate may claim a range of removal and other expenses directly from the FHSA or Health Board, subject to certain qualifying conditions.

The Red Book also specifies that two-thirds of an associate's subscription to a professional defence organisation will be reimbursed, and provides for payment of the postgraduate education allowance. It describes how the schemes for additional payments during confinement or sickness apply to both the associate and employing practitioners.

7 Absence from Practice

Additional payments during sickness

IF a GP is away from the practice owing to illness, he or she will continue to receive normal remuneration and may also be eligible to receive an additional allowance to help towards the costs of employing a locum or deputy from outside the practice. Eligibility for these payments depends largely on list size. The addition may not pay the full cost of the locum, and the GP will have to pay the rest.

The scheme applies to GPs under 70 years of age, in receipt of a BPA, who provide unrestricted general medical services. If less than a full BPA is being paid, the payment for sickness will be correspondingly reduced.

Doctors aged between 70 and 72 years receive only limited payments.

Practitioners in receipt of an associate allowance may in certain circumstances qualify for help with the cost of employing a locum during an associate's absence through sickness.

Scale of payments

The payment varies according to the GP's length of service (*see* Box 7.1).

Box 7.1: Additional payments during sickness: scale of payments	
Length of service	*Scale of payment*
During first year	One month's payment and (after completing four months' service) 2 months' half payment
During second year	2 months' full payment and 2 months' half payment
During third year	4 months' full payment and 4 months' half payment
During fourth and fifth years	5 months' full payment and 5 months' half payment
After completing 5 years' service	6 months' full payment and 6 months' half payment

When an application is accepted, the appropriate payment is calculated by deducting from the period of benefit appropriate to the doctor's service on the first day of absence the total period for which payment has already been made during the preceding twelve months.

The meaning of the term 'service' and the conditions relating to breaks in service, are defined in the Red Book.

'Service' includes periods as an unrestricted principal, full-time assistant, trainee or associate doctor, and employment in certain hospital posts and other posts approved for the purposes of the NHS Superannuation Regulations.

In exceptional circumstances, the Secretary of State may agree to extend payments beyond 6 months at the full rate and 6 months at the half rate to a GP with at least 5 years' service.

Conditions of payment

Payments are made only when one or more locums or deputies from outside the practice are employed. It is accepted that a single-handed GP will normally need to engage a locum or deputy when incapacitated. However, if a single-handed GP employs an assistant, the assistant will be expected to cover the practice unaided for up to 4 weeks, provided the list is no greater than 2700 patients. Doctors working in partnerships or groups will be expected to cover for each other as far as possible, and additional payments will be made only if the GP's absence leaves the remaining doctors with a high average number of patients to care for (*see* box 7.2).

Box 7.2: Average number of patients per remaining partner required to qualify for additional payments during sickness			
Duration or expected duration of incapacity	*Average number of patients*		
	Full-time practitioner	Three-quarter-time practitioner	Half-time practitioner
Not more than 2 weeks	3600 or more	2700 or more	1800 or more
Not more than 6 weeks	3100 or more	2325 or more	1550 or more
Longer than 6 weeks	2700 or more	2025 or more	1350 or more

In calculating each of the others' average number of patients, an FHSA will assume each part-time practitioner has on his or her personal list the number of patients set out above. Once these figures have been deducted from the total partnership or group list, the balance will be averaged between the remaining GPs. If a partnership or group employs a full-time assistant (or equivalent part-time assistants) other than a trainee practitioner, the assistant will be deemed to be able to care for up to 2700 patients, and this number will be deducted from the total number of patients on the lists of the partners or group members before calculating the average number of patients to be cared for by the remaining partners or group members. Similarly, if a partnership or group employs a part-time assistant, the assistant will be deemed to be able to care for that proportion of 2700 patients which corresponds to the proportion of part-time hours the assistant works compared with a full-time commitment.

The FHSA, after consulting the LMC, may waive these requirements if the practice has to cover a large geographical area, or the GPs' ages or health inhibit their capacity to take on the additional workload, or unusually high rates of sickness are prevalent in the practice area.

No payments are made if the period of incapacity is less than a week, or if a GP is absent because of an accident and financial compensation may be recovered.

Payments under the scheme require the submission of medical certificates to the FHSA. The GP must agree to be examined by a doctor nominated by the FHSA if this is requested.

Box 7.3: Additional payments during sickness

1 The addition is a contribution towards the cost of employing a locum or deputy from outside the practice
2 Eligibility depends on the length of absence and the number of patients registered with the practice
3 The scale of payments depends on the GP's length of service

---

Basis of payment

A full-time GP eligible to receive full payments who employs a full-time locum or deputy (i.e. working 'normal' hours, on at least 5 days a week or the equivalent spread over 6 days) from outside the practice, will be reimbursed the actual amount paid or the maximum allowance, whichever is the less.

A part-time GP will receive a reduced level of reimbursement: either half or three-quarters of the maximum, depending on his or her availability. Payments are also reduced if the locum is employed less than full-time.

Payments are calculated according to a different formula if the deputy is a principal on an FHSA medical list. Although the same overall limit applies, payment is calculated at a maximum rate representing three-quarters of the standard capitation fees earned by the sick GP. More than one locum or deputy may be employed, but total reimbursement will not exceed that paid for one full-time equivalent. These reimbursements may be abated if the GP's private practice income exceeds 10% of his or her total practice income.

Assistants

If a GP employs an assistant for whom an allowance is being paid, additional payments during sickness may be available in certain circumstances if the assistant falls ill.

Additional payments during confinement

A similar scheme to that for sickness payments applies to women GPs who are absent owing to pregnancy and childbirth. These payments supplement normal remuneration, and are paid to a GP who remains on the medical list and intends to continue in general practice. Payments are made only if a locum or deputy from outside the practice is engaged to care for patients.

Eligibility

All women GPs providing unrestricted general medical services and in receipt of a BPA are eligible. A part-time GP can claim reduced payments: half or three-quarters of the maximum allowance depending on her availability.

Duration of payments

Payments are made for a maximum of 13 weeks, although the GP may be away for a longer period. It is expected that the date of confinement will normally fall midway in the 13 week period. Many doctors ask their FHSA if they can have a longer period of absence (for which claims are to be made) after the confinement than before. FHSAs' responses to these requests vary; most are prepared to agree provided that the health of the expectant mother is not at risk. A doctor who is absent because of illness before or after the 13 week period covered by this scheme may also be eligible to claim additional payments during sickness.

Under the new GP contract, eligibility for payments under this scheme is no longer related to list size.

The GP must state that she intends to return to general practice within a reasonable period after the birth.

Box 7.4: Additional payments during confinement

1 Eligibility is not affected by the practice list size
2 Payments are made for 13 weeks, and it is expected that the date of confinement will fall roughly midway
3 The applicant must declare her intention to return to general practice after the birth

---

Claims

Claims should be made early in pregnancy, and must be accompanied by a Certificate of Expected Confinement or a comparable private certificate.

Absence of assistants

A doctor who is being paid an assistant's allowance may be able to claim payments under this scheme for employing outside help during the assistant's confinement.

Locum allowance for single-handed practitioners in rural areas attending educational courses

A single-handed doctor receiving rural practice payments who is absent from the practice attending an accredited postgraduate educational course may be eligible to receive a special payment in addition to normal remuneration, towards paying a locum or other deputy doctor engaged to look after the practice in his or her absence.

Eligibility

The scheme applies to single-handed doctors receiving rural practice payments, except those with an associate allowance. (They are expected to arrange for their associate doctor to look after the practice while they attend a postgraduate course.) The course attended must be accredited as of at least a full day's duration.

Payment will be made only if a locum is actually and necessarily engaged to provide cover, for travelling time as well as time on the course.

However, if a doctor already employs an assistant, the assistant will be expected to look after the practice unaided for up to 4 weeks, if the list size is no more than 2700.

Basis of payment

If a locum is engaged who is not a principal on an FHSA medical list, the payments the doctor has made to the locum will be reimbursed up to the weekly maximum indicated in the Red Book. If the principal doctor is absent for less than 1 week, payments made to the locum will be reimbursed at up to one fifth of the weekly rate for every full day for which the locum was engaged, up to the weekly maximum.

If the locum is on an FHSA medical list and has his or her own practice, payment will be subject to a maximum rate representing three quarters of the standard capitation fees (including the higher rates for elderly patients) due to the absent GP.

If a GP engages more than one locum to cover absence, the maximum figure reimbursed cannot exceed the figure paid for a single locum. If one locum is on a medical list and one is not, then the respective reimbursements will be calculated as set out in the previous two paragraphs.

Payments will not be abated if the gross income from private practice undertaken by the doctor is less than 10% of total practice income. If gross receipts from private practice are greater, payments will be abated by 10% if 10% but not more than 20% of gross receipts are from private practice, by 20% if 20% but not more than 30% are, and so on.

However, if a locum does not cover for any private work or is not qualified to do so and the FHSA accepts that is so, it excludes from the calculation described in the last paragraph income from work which the locum does not undertake for the absent doctor.

It is important to ensure that expenses incurred when employing a locum are shown gross in the practice accounts and that payments from the FHSA are shown as income, in the same way as capitation fees and other receipts.

Claims for payment

A doctor's responsible FHSA will make the reimbursement and provide application and claim forms.

It is important for a GP to apply to the FHSA as soon as a locum has been arranged, so that the FHSA can let the doctor know as soon as possible whether the application has been accepted.

Claims for payment should be submitted when practice is resumed or when the locum's employment ends, whichever is the earlier. The certificate on the reverse side of the form must be completed and signed by each locum for whom payment is claimed.

If there is a change in locum arrangements, the FHSA must be informed immediately. The submission of further claims should await acceptance of the revised arrangements under the scheme.

Allowances for prolonged study leave

Although it is included in the Red Book, this scheme remains little known and thus hardly used. It provides financial assistance to a GP who takes prolonged study leave which is considered to be in the interests of medicine or of the NHS as a whole. Each application is considered on its merits, but the study should be different in scope and depth from a refresher course and be capable of significantly extending the GP's professional or administrative skills and knowledge. Study leave solely for the purpose of obtaining a higher professional qualification will not normally be eligible.

Essential features of the scheme are as follows.

1 The length of absence should normally be between 10 weeks and 12 months.
2 Payments under the scheme take the form of an educational allowance and, where applicable, a contribution towards the cost of employing a locum or deputy from outside the practice.
3 If a locum allowance is paid, it is calculated in a similar way to that in the scheme for additional payments during sickness. However, there are no list size criteria.
4 Applications are handled by the Regional Postgraduate Dean, who forwards these, together with the views of the Regional Postgraduate Committee, to the Secretary of State, who then determines whether a payment is made.

Box 7.5: Allowances for prolonged study leave

1 Absence on prolonged study leave normally lasts between 10 weeks and 12 months
2 Payments take the form of an educational allowance and, if appropriate, a locum allowance
3 Eligibility for a locum allowance is unrelated to list size
4 Applications, submitted via the Regional Postgraduate Dean, are determined by the Secretary of State

---

Advice can be obtained from the Regional Adviser in General Practice or the FHSA.

Temporary arrangements for carrying on a practice

The National Health Service (General Medical and Pharmaceutical Services) Regulations 1974, as amended, which include the terms of service for doctors, contain certain provisions relating to the temporary care of patients whose GP has ceased to be included in the medical list. The payments to be made to a GP appointed to care for these patients under Regulations 19(2) and 19(6) are explained in paragraphs 78 and 79 of the Red Book.

8 Capitation Fees and Calculation of Lists

STANDARD capitation fees are paid at three rates according to a patient's age on the last day of the preceding quarter:

- under 65 years
- 65 to 74 years
- 75 years and over.

Fees are paid quarterly at one quarter of the annual rate. (Capitation fees for child health surveillance and deprivation are also paid quarterly at one quarter of the annual rate.)

The calculation of lists is described in paragraph 73 of the Red Book. Under the new contract arrangements patients' ages are calculated quarterly, and not annually as previously. As soon as possible after the beginning of each quarter, the FHSA will notify the GP of:

1 the number of patients on his or her list in each of the three age groups;
2 the number of children for whom he or she has agreed to provide child health surveillance;
3 the number of patients for whom a deprivation payment is due, in each group, and the level of fee they attract;
4 the number of patients for whom a rural practice payment is due.

If the FHSA is notified of a patient's acceptance within 48 hours of the beginning of a quarter, and is satisfied that the patient was accepted by the practitioner on or before the first day of the quarter, the patient will be included in the count of patients on the first day of the quarter. Every GP should send acceptances to the FHSA as soon as possible. This helps the FHSA spread its workload, increases the accuracy of the count at the start of the quarter, and makes an important contribution towards speeding up the transfer of medical records between practitioners.

Challenging the FHSA's estimate of list size

A GP who wishes to challenge the FHSA's count of patients must give notice to the FHSA of such a challenge within 10 days of receiving notification of the numbers on his or her list. Objections to the count cannot be made after this 10 day period. Having given notice of a challenge, the GP should submit to the FHSA, within 21 days of the receipt of the original notification, any evidence that may reasonably be required to settle the dispute.

Box 8.1: Challenging the FHSA's count of a list of patients

1 Notice of challenge must be submitted within 10 days of the receipt of notification of the list size
2 The onus is on the GP to submit evidence to challenge the FHSA's figures. Such evidence must be submitted within 21 days of the receipt of notification of list size

9 Deprivation Payments

Eligibility

A doctor providing general medical services to a patient on the doctor's list who resides in an area identified as deprived for the purposes of this payment will be eligible to receive a deprivation payment for that patient. Deprived areas will be determined by the Secretary of State following consultation with the profession, and FHSAs will inform GPs of these.

Level and method of payment

The FHSA will pay the appropriate level of fee on the first day of each quarter in respect of each patient who attracts a deprivation payment. There are three levels of payment, according to the extent of deprivation in the area where the patient lives.

10 Initial Practice Allowances and Inducement Payments

Initial Practice Allowances

INITIAL Practice Allowances are paid to support certain practices which are considered to be essential to meet patients' needs but are not otherwise viable. There are two types of Initial Practice Allowance (IPA).

Type 1 for single-handed practices in designated areas

This allowance is available to full-time and job sharing practitioners genuinely setting up a new single-handed practice, or filling a vacancy in a small single-handed practice, in a medical practice area which is designated.

A 'small single-handed' practice is one in which the annual income from capitation fees including deprivation payments and, where appropriate, child health surveillance fees and basic practice allowance, calculated on the size of the list at the date of succeeding to the vacancy, could fall short of the allowance in the first year to a practitioner setting up a new practice.

Eligibility

In order to qualify for the allowance a practitioner must either have been:

1 in general practice for a total period of not less than 1 year as a principal, or trainee; or
2 fully registered as a medical practitioner for a period of not less than 3 years.

Payment

The allowance is paid for up to 4 years and ensures that the practice receives a guaranteed minimum income. In simplified terms the allowance is paid in accordance with the scale detailed in the Red Book, and if the practitioner is succeeding to an established practice, he or she receives the allowance less the income which the practice attracts by way of capitation fees, deprivation payments, child health surveillance fees and basic practice allowance (excluding additions) that are payable in respect of the patients transferred to the incoming practitioner. In subsequent years there is no differentiation between the payments to practitioners who have set up a new practice, and those who have succeeded to an existing practice: the allowance is paid minus the income the practice attracts in the normal way from capitation fees etc.

There are of course currently no designated areas in England and Wales and therefore no new Initial Practice Allowances of Type 1 can be paid.

Type 2 for practices in special areas

This allowance will be offered in areas selected and approved by the Department in consultation with the MPC having regard to reports from FHSAs, who will themselves have consulted LMCs. Type 2 allowances are considered appropriate for areas of major housing development where considerable population increase in a comparatively few years is expected, and where it is desirable at the outset to have full time practitioners of experience and personal qualities to establish general practice and build up a sizeable team working in conjunction with other health services in the area. The area might for example be a new development planned to grow to a population of 15 000 or more and requiring a team of 5 to 8 practitioners.

The first and second practitioners must be full time as must the majority of the other practitioners.

The availability of existing local practices able to expand and provide a good service to a new area might make it unnecessary to consider payment of a Type 2 allowance.

The allowance will provide a guaranteed net income at flat rates for both the first and second practitioner in a practice recognized as attracting a Type 2 allowance. It will be payable for up to 5 years from the date the first practitioner takes up his or her appointment.

Appointment of practitioners

The first practitioner will be appointed by the Medical Practices Committee following the advertizing of the post. The practitioner will normally have been qualified for 10 years, and have spent 2 years in hospital appointments and 5 years in a busy general practice in this country.

The second practitioner will normally be appointed as a partner to the first practitioner and the usual arrangements for filling a partnership vacancy will apply.

Full details of the scheme, including how the allowance is calculated, are given in paras. 41.12 to 41.21 of the Red Book.

Initial Practice Allowances: preserved rights

Doctors who at 31 March 1990 were eligible for either a Type B or Type C Initial Practice Allowance under the provisions of paragraph 40 of the Red Book in force at that time will continue to receive these allowances as long as they remain on the medical list of an FHSA and satisfy the qualifying conditions.

Type B allowance – rates of allowance: second year

For the second year starting on or after 1 April 1990 the relevant amounts shown under item 13(ii) of paragraph 1/sch.1 of the old Red Book in force at 31 March 1990 are set out in the schedule to paragraph 81 of the new Red Book.

Type B allowance – reckonable income

For the year commencing April 1990, notional amounts for vocational training and group practice allowances, for the purposes of calculating 'total reckonable income' as in paragraph 40.9(i) of the old Red Book in force on 31 March 1990 are set out in the schedule to paragraph 81 of the new Red Book. Amounts for seniority addition and practice in a designated area are shown at items 2(ii) and (i) of paragraph 1/sch.1 of the new Red Book.

Type C allowance – rates of allowance

The amounts for the 4 years of a Type C allowance are shown in the schedule attached to paragraph 81 of the new Red Book.

Inducement payments

Eligibility and payment

An inducement payment will be available for full-time or job sharing practitioners practising in an area where the FHSA, after consultation with the Medical Practices Committee, has accepted that it is essential to maintain a medical practice although the area is sparsely populated or is for some other reason unattractive to a practitioner.

Very few inducement payments are made in England and Wales.

A practitioner who wishes to be considered for this payment should contact the FHSA. Assessment of eligibility and of any sum payable will be determined by the Secretary of State on the individual merits of each case and will be reviewed annually.

Seniority Allowance, Associate Allowance and Sickness Payments

For the purposes of Seniority Allowance, Associate Allowance and Sickness Payments a doctor who receives an inducement payment will be treated as if he or she has at least 1200 patients.

11 Rural Practice Payments

THIS scheme provides for payments to be made to eligible GPs from a central fund determined on an annual basis. The total amount of money available is divided by the number of units credited to GPs throughout England and Wales, and the payment to each individual GP is calculated by multiplying the number of units to which the GP is entitled by the value of each unit.

Eligibility

A GP may have rural practice units credited for payment if he or she has at least 10% of patients on his or her own list resident in a rural practice area and living at least 3 miles from the main surgery by the normal route. The eligibility of doctors in partnership is assessed individually. If the proportion of rural practice patients falls below 10%, the GP ceases to be eligible for payment; however, if the drop is not below 9%, the FHSA may extend payments for not more than 4 successive quarters.

Rural practice areas are determined by the FHSA, which can give advice about each locality.

All calculations are based on the distance from the main surgery; if a GP has a number of surgeries and there is some doubt about which is the main surgery, the FHSA will determine the premises from which the rural practice units are calculated, in consultation with the LMC. In making their decision, they will take into account surgery times and the number of patients seen and will give the GP the opportunity to comment. If there are any substantial changes in the practice, a GP may apply or the FHSA may decide to alter the surgery from which rural practice payments are calculated, but before doing so the FHSA will consult the LMC and the GP, and the GP will be given notice of the change. A doctor in group practice will have his or her rural practice units calculated from the group main surgery unless the GP spends less than half of his or her total surgery time at the group main surgery in which case the above provisions will apply.

Calculation of units

A GP eligible for rural practice payments will be credited with the appropriate amount of units calculated on the first day of each quarter.

Reinstatements or removals from the list relating to the previous quarter received after the second day or up to the end of the first month of the new quarter will be taken into account retrospectively.

Each patient resident in a Rural Practice Area will attract units on the following grounds:

1 distance
2 walking
3 difficult walking
4 blocked route
5 residence in a Special District.

Units for distance and walking will be credited only for those patients in a Rural Practice Area who live not less than 3 miles from the GP's main surgery by the normal outward route.

Distance units are calculated as follows:

for at least 3 miles but less than 4 miles	: 1 unit
for at least 4 miles but less than 5 miles	: 3 units
for at least 5 miles but less than 6 miles	: 5 units
for each additional mile or part of a mile	: 2 additional units.

Walking units will be credited in addition to the above for that part of the route which has to be walked. The distance is calculated from the point where the GP would have to leave an ordinary two-wheel-drive car and walk to the patient's residence under normal winter conditions. Walking units are calculated as follows:

for at least a quarter of a mile but less than half a mile:	3 units
for at least half a mile but less than three-quarters of a mile	: 6 units
for each additional quarter of a mile or part of a quarter of a mile	: 3 additional units.

Units for difficult walking, blocked route or residence in a Special District will be credited in respect of patients resident in a Rural Practice Area *irrespective of whether* the distance from the main surgery is as much as 3 miles as long as the following conditions are satisfied.

Difficult walking units will be credited if the GP has to walk for not less than one-quarter of a mile of the normal outward route between the main surgery and the patient's residence under conditions involving exceptional difficulties, for example, because part of the route is very steep, rough or boggy. The units will be credited only for the part of the distance that involves the exceptional difficulty, and at the following rates:

for at least quarter of a mile but less than half a mile	: 4 units
for at least half a mile but less than three-quarters of a mile	: 6 units

for each additional quarter of a mile or part of a
quarter mile   : 2 additional units.

Blocked route units will be credited if the normal route from the GP's main surgery is regularly liable at certain seasons of the year to be blocked owing to flooding or other severe weather conditions. Three units will be credited for each patient affected whatever the distance from the main surgery.

The Central Advisory Committee advised the Secretary of State for Health on areas designated as a Special District such as those where climatic and geographical conditions are such that not only are there difficulties of access for which walking and difficult walking units are given but there are also difficulties for travelling by road. Doctors will be notified by the FHSA of Special Districts and will receive 4 units per patient in the district regardless of distance. A GP cannot be credited for a patient resident in a Special District as well as for the same patient in respect of a blocked route.

The FHSA maintains a register of schools, hospitals and other institutions in Rural Practice Areas where there are normally more than 25 patients registered. The units to be credited for these patients will be half the prescribed rate. A list of those institutions is notifed to the GPs concerned. Patients in smaller institutions attract units at the full rate.

Units to be credited for patients not on a GP's list

Credit for units relating to temporary residents, emergency visits and patients receiving immediately necessary treatment will be given. Details are set out in paragraphs 43.12 and 43.13 of the Red Book.

Rural practice payments not on the basis of units

Any GP can claim refunds of out-of-pocket expenses actually and necessarily incurred in travelling to visit a patient in a Rural Practice Area if the FHSA is satisfied that the expenses were of an exceptional nature, for example ferry charges, boat hire charges or toll charges. Where it is not possible for a GP to produce receipts, he or she will be required to submit a certified statement of expendiure.

Submission of claims

It is important that GPs include on their acceptance document for the patient any claim that they wish to make for patient payments even if at the time they are not eligible for the payment. The FHSA will then credit its record system with the information as there may come a time when the GP becomes eligible if 10% of his or her patients are resident in a Rural Practice Area. The FHSA is under no obligation to complete the claim for a doctor who omits to show that a rural practice claim is appropriate.

12 Maternity Medical Services

Fees—general

The fees paid for Maternity Medical Services (MMS) are listed in the Red Book. A doctor *not* included in the Obstetric List who is providing these services to his or her own patients is paid a much lower level of fees than a doctor who is included. In addition, the obstetrically approved doctor can accept women for MMS who are not included in his or her ordinary list of patients.

To gain admission to the Obstetric List, a GP must have his or her experience in obstetrics approved by the Local Obstetric Committee or the Secretary of State for Health.

How does a GP gain admission to the Obstetric List?

Criteria determining entry to the Obstetric List are set out in paragraph 31 of the Red Book.

The most common qualification is to have held a 6 months' resident appointment in a hospital obstetric unit in the UK or the Republic of Ireland, or a similar appointment in a British Armed Forces hospital obstetric unit overseas.

Less commonly approved is experience in a UK hospital obstetric unit under consultant supervision during 6 consecutive months in the 2 years prior to making an application to the FHSA. This particular criterion specifies the number of normal deliveries, abnormal confinements and clinics which a GP should have attended.

If a GP has undertaken a 6 months' obstetric post more than 10 years prior to applying, he or she would need to have attended, as a minimum, a week's refresher course within the previous 5 years, or spent not less than 2 weeks as a resident obstetric officer in a UK obstetric unit under consultant supervision.

There are 4 other entry criteria. If, when applying for inclusion in the Obstetric List, a GP is already included in another FHSA's Obstetric List, the application will be accepted. Similarly, if during the previous 2 years a doctor has been included in an Obstetric List because of having held a resident 6 month post, the application would also be accepted. If a GP can demonstrate having been a principal in obstetric practice in the UK and attending not less than 100 maternity cases over the previous 5 years, during the care of which cases he or she was responsible for ante-natal care in all and the supervision of labour and puerperium in at least 50, he or she would be accepted. Finally, the Secretary of State has the power to approve an application on the recommendation of the Local Obstetric Committee if the GP's experience does not meet any of the above criteria but is considered acceptable.

Box 12.1: Qualifying for the Obstetric List

1 Six months' post
2 Attendance at a consultant unit during 6 consecutive months
3 On another FPC Obstetric List
4 On an Obstetric List during previous 2 years
5 Previous obstetric experience in general practice
6 Secretary of State's approval of previous experience

Guidance on fees

Ante-natal care fees

There are three levels of fee payable, and these are not affected if the patient receives any hospital care. They are paid if she is confined after the 28th week, or earlier if a live birth results.

1 That for a woman booking up to the 16th week of pregnancy.
2 That for a woman booking from the 17th to the 30th week of pregnancy.
3 That for a woman booking from the 31st week of pregnancy.

The date of booking is taken as the date on which the woman signs the acceptance application in Part II of form FP24/24A.

Miscarriage fee

If a woman's pregnancy ends during or before the 28th week and does not result in a live birth, a miscarriage fee is paid for any MMS provided.

Abortion

Making arrangements for a therapeutic abortion is part of general medical services. However, if the need for an abortion arises after the patient has been accepted for MMS, a miscarriage fee is paid for any maternity services given prior to the decision that there should be an abortion. Post-operative care of a woman after an abortion does *not* qualify for post-natal care fees.

Confinement fee

This fee is paid for providing MMS during a confinement, and includes cases where a GP is called during labour to a patient who is not booked for MMS with the GP.

Premature confinement

A premature confinement after the 28th week, or at any other time if it results in a live birth, is treated as a confinement at full term and the appropriate fees are paid.

Post-natal care fees

Complete fee

A GP who provides MMS to mother and child throughout the 14 days immediately after confinement and carries out a full post-natal examination at or about 6 weeks after confinement, is paid the complete post-natal care fee. The full post-natal examination must normally be undertaken within 12 weeks of confinement. The complete fee will still be paid if the patient is confined in a hospital other than a GP unit, provided the woman leaves hospital—either to return home or to a GP maternity unit—not later than the second day after delivery.

Partial fee

A fee is paid to a GP for each attendance to give medical care to either the mother or her child during the 14 days after the birth, **but** fees are paid only for a maximum of 5 such attendances. A fee is also paid for a full post-natal examination at or about 6 weeks after confinement. This is paid if the examination is carried out up to 12 weeks after confinement. However, if a GP submits a claim for a fee for an examination carried out later than 12 weeks, the FHSA needs to be satisfied that the doctor has carried it out as soon as possible and has made reasonable efforts to undertake the examination between 6 and 12 weeks after confinement for the fee to be paid. The Department of Health has advised FHSAs that no payment should be made for an examination carried out within 4 weeks of confinement, and that a case would have to be made for payment sooner than 6 weeks after the confinement. It is important to emphasize that where a patient has been confined either at home or in hospital and requires medical attendance *beyond* the fourteenth day after her confinement, her own GP should provide this as part of general medical services.

What can be claimed if a post-natal examination is not undertaken?

If a GP has otherwise provided complete care, but because of circumstances beyond the doctor's control the post-natal examination had not been carried out, the FHSA may pay the full fee if it is satisfied that the doctor made 'reasonable efforts' to undertake the examination. Efforts accepted by a FHSA as reasonable might include 2 letters from the GP to the patient requesting her to attend the surgery for the examination, followed by either a request to the patient through a health visitor or midwife, or a call by the doctor at the patient's home.

Complete MMS fee

The complete MMS fee is paid to a GP who provides complete MMS during pregnancy, confinement and the post-natal period and carries out a full post-natal examination at or about 6 weeks after confinement. This examination must normally be carried out no later than 12 weeks after confinement. If a GP provides complete MMS to a woman and has accepted her at least 6 weeks before confinement the full fee is paid.

Fee for second practitioner giving an anaesthetic

If a GP providing MMS calls a second doctor to give an anaesthetic, an additional fee will be payable. The doctor will still be entitled to that fee if for good professional reasons the second practitioner carries out the delivery and the GP who called him or her administers the anaesthetic. An anaesthetic fee is *not* payable if the anaesthetic is administered by a trainee GP for his or her trainer or for the trainer's partner or assistant. Normally, only one fee is paid for a particular confinement, even if an anaesthetic is administered more than once. If, exceptionally, two separate and distinct attendances are necessary to administer an anaesthetic, a further fee is paid.

Box 12.2: MMS: specific fees payable

1 Complete services
2 Ante-natal care
3 Miscarriage
4 Confinement
5 Post-natal care
6 For second practitioner giving an anaesthetic

Second opinion

If a GP refers a patient to a consultant for a second opinion he or she remains entitled to the appropriate fees so long as responsibility for the patient's maternity care is retained.

What happens if a patient accepted for maternity care receives MMS from another doctor?

There may be circumstances in which a patient accepted by a GP for maternity care receives care from another GP, for instance if she temporarily lives in another area. When this occurs, the total amount paid is limited to either the fee for complete MMS, or a smaller fee appropriate for the actual services provided. For example, if a woman resides in another area for some time and a doctor in that area provides some MMS care then the main or 'responsible' FHSA may agree with the 'temporary' FHSA that the fees are divided proportionately between the two GPs in accordance with the care provided (*see* Box 12.3). A similar approach is adopted if a woman moves permanently during maternity care, whether the move is within an FHSA area or from one FHSA area to another.

Claims for payment

Claims for payment are made to the FHSA for the area in which the patient resides. For GPs on the Obstetric List, form FP24 is completed, and for GPs not on the Obstetric List, form FP24A. Part II of the form (application for services) must be completed and signed by the patient and Part III by the doctor, **but** Part II contains a special certificate for the doctor to use if he or she attends a woman in an emergency and considers it undesirable to ask for her signature.

Normally, the GP's certificate on the claim form is sufficient evidence of services having been provided, but in cases of doubt the FHSA may make enquiries before authorizing payment. For example, in the case of a claim for a complete fee, if the FHSA, after consultation with the LMC, is not satisfied that complete MMS were provided, it may pay the appropriate partial care fees instead.

Completion of claim forms

If forms FP24 and FP24A are completed accurately and submitted promptly, it helps both GPs and FHSAs. Most FHSAs process MMS claims by computer and it is therefore most important that claim forms are completed accurately. Form FP24 is shown in Fig. 12.1, and attention is drawn to those parts of the form which often lead to queries.

Box 12.3: Example of apportionment of fees between two GPs providing MMS to one woman

Both GPs on the Obstetric List

Expected date of confinement 16 October 1990

Dr A: Patient booked for MMS 25 April 1990 (15th week)
      Patient subsequently moved temporarily
Dr B: Patient booked for MMS 5 July 1990 (25th week)
      Patient returned home 38th week
Dr A: Care during confinement on 15 October 1990
      + post-natal care
      + post-natal examination at 6th week after confinement

Payment for ante-natal care

			Dr A	Dr B
1st level	Dr A:	(15th week)	£19.60	
2nd level	Dr A:	8/13 × £19.55	£12.03	
	Dr B:	5/13 × £19.55 (25th week)		£ 7.52
3rd level	Dr A:	2/9 × £39.15	£ 8.70	
	Dr B:	7/9 × £39.15		£30.45
			£40.33	£37.97

Total payment made: £78.30

Payment for confinement and post-natal care

Dr A:
Care during confinement			£33.35
Complete post-natal:	(i)	5 visits @ £4.45 during 14 days puerperium	£22.25
	(ii)	post-natal pelvic examination at or about the 6th week	£11.10
			£66.70

Dr A is paid	£107.03
Dr B is paid	£ 37.97
Total fees paid	£145.00

NB: For apportionment purposes of ante-natal:
1st level (£78.30 – £58.70)	£19.60
2nd level (£58.70 – £39.15)	£19.55
3rd level	£39.15
	£78.30

NATIONAL HEALTH SERVICE   **MATERNITY MEDICAL SERVICES** .

PART I

(to be detached and given to the patient)

To ....

I accept your application to receive maternity medical services from me.

Your expected date of confinement is ....

Date ....   Doctor's signature ....

PART II

PATIENT'S APPLICATION FOR SERVICES

(Tick appropriate box)

Dr. ....

A   I wish to receive maternity medical services from you. I have not made arrangements for these services with another doctor.   ☐

B   I wish to receive maternity medical services from you. I have cancelled arrangements

made with Dr. ....

of ....   ☐

C   I wish to receive maternity medical services from you whilst temporarily residing at:

....

....   ☐

I have made arrangements for maternity medical services in my home area with

Dr. ....

....

D   I have received maternity medical services from you in an emergency.   ☐

Patient's full name ....
(in block letters)

Home address ....

....

Former name ....   N.H.S. No. ❶ ....
                                                                  or Date of Birth

Date ....   Patient's signature ....

DOCTOR'S CERTIFICATE

(EMERGENCY ATTENDANCE FOR MISCARRIAGE)

I certify that in the circumstances I thought it desirable, in the patient's interest, not to ask her for a signature.

Date ....   Doctor's signature ....

Form **FP24**

Figure 12.1.

MATERNITY BENEFITS

There are cash benefits for mothers under the National Insurance Scheme which must be claimed within certain time limits. You are strongly advised to get Leaflet N.I. 17A and the necessary claim form from your local Maternity and Child Health Clinic, or from your local Department of Health and Social Security office not later than 14 weeks before your baby is expected.

PRESCRIPTION CHARGES AND WELFARE MILK AND VITAMINS

An expectant mother can apply on Part 1 of the Certificate of Pregnancy (Form FW8) for a prescription charge exemption certificate covering the period of her pregnancy and until her child is one year old. Details are given on Part 2 of Form FW8 and in leaflet MV11 (obtainable from Post Offices, local Department of Health and Social Security offices and local Maternity and Child Health Clinics) of how to claim free milk and vitamins.

PART III
DOCTOR'S CERTIFICATE AND CLAIM FOR PAYMENT
(References are to paragraphs in the Statement of Fees and Allowances)

(Tick appropriate box)

I certify that...(patient's name)

(expected date of confinement........❷.......)   had a miscarriage on ....❸..... ☐
                                                    was confined on .... ☐

at home.. ☐
In the GP Unit at ....❹... Hospital ☐
In... Hospital ☐

I further certify that I provided the services indicated below and that I had regard to and was guided by authoritative medical opinion as set out in paragraphs 31.2 and paragraph 31/Schedule 3.

(i) Complete Maternity Medical Services ❺.................... Paras 31.7 to 31.8 ☐
(ii) Ante-natal care

Note: the date of booking is the date on which Parts I and II are completed

(a) Patient booked up to 16th week of pregnancy .... Para 31.9 ☐
(b) Patient booked from 17th week to 30th week
    of pregnancy .... **Para 31.9** ☐
(c) Patient booked from 31st week of pregnancy .... **Para 31.9** ☐

(iii) Miscarriage .... Para 31.10 ☐
(iv) Care during the confinement..........❻............... Para 31.11 ☐
(v) Complete Post-Natal Care (Date of Hospital Discharge ❼.....) Para 31.12 ☐
(vi) Partial Post-Natal Care .... Para 31.13 ☐
    (a) date of each attendance

(b) date of full post-natal examination ❽...........................
(vii) Other services as described in the attached note... ☐

(viii) Date of last service to patient..
(to be completed where only ante-natal care or only complete post-natal care is given).

I claim payment for the above services... ☐

I also claim payment for the employment as anaesthetist of Dr............................ ☐
                                                        Paras 31.15 to 31.16

Date.............................   Doctor's signature..

Fees approved for payment £

Figure 12.1. Key:
[1] please enter correct NHS number;
[2] please enter this date other than when claiming for post-natal care only;
[3] it is important that these dates are *clearly* entered as appropriate;
[4] please enter these sections correctly because different fees are payable;
[5] this section must be completed when complete care is provided;
[6] this section should be completed *only* when a woman has been confined at home or in a GP unit;
[7] this section should be completed *only* when a woman is confined in hospital (other than a GP unit) for less than 48 hours;
[8] this section should be completed when partial care is given.

Responsibilities of general practitioners under the contract

The Regulations specify the arrangements and conditions according to which maternity medical services are provided.

Services for a woman permanently living in a general practitioner's practice area

A GP who has agreed to provide MMS for a woman is responsible for ensuring that she receives all necessary medical services during pregnancy, confinement and the post-natal period. This obligation applies from when she is accepted for maternity care until 14 days after her confinement. However, where a woman is booked into a hospital for confinement, the hospital staff are responsible for her care during that period (unless she is in a GP maternity unit to which the GP has access). The GP is also responsible for making a full post-natal examination at or about 6 weeks after confinement and certainly no later than 12 weeks after confinement (save in exceptional circumstances as explained on page 64).

If a pregnancy is terminated by a miscarriage, a GP is responsible for providing care from when the woman is accepted for MMS until the miscarriage.

If a patient moves out of a GP's practice area, then unless the GP agrees to continue care, he or she is responsible for her care only from the time she is accepted for maternity care until the time she leaves the area.

Services for a woman temporarily residing in a general practitioner's practice area

If a GP accepts a woman for maternity care who is living temporarily in the practice area, then the doctor's responsibility for her care is the same as if she lived there permanently. The doctor is also responsible for advising a woman on how to arrange continuing treatment if she leaves the area.

Good maternal and early neonatal care

A practitioner providing maternity care is required to certify that in providing services he or she has had regard to and been guided by modern authoritative medical opinion.

13 Contraceptive Services

Two types of fee are paid to GPs for providing contraceptive services: the ordinary fee and an intrauterine device fee. The fees are paid at annual rates representing payment for services over a 12-month period. FHSAs pay quarterly ordinary fees of one-quarter of the annual amount. Intrauterine device fees are also paid quarterly, but the first payment is at a higher rate than the other three quarterly payments to provide a fee for fitting the device. Any woman—not only a woman registered for general medical services—can apply to be accepted as a contraceptive patient.

Conditions for payment

Ordinary fee

The ordinary fee is paid when a GP accepts a patient, gives advice and conducts any necessary examination, where appropriate prescribes drugs or an occlusive cap and provides any necessary follow-up care. The doctor can also claim the fee if he or she helps the patient choose a method of contraception and accepts responsibility for any necessary aftercare, even though the advice may be to attend an NHS clinic for the fitting of an occlusive cap or intrauterine device. This means that even if a woman attends the surgery and advice is given about a male contraceptive or vasectomy, a GP may still claim if he or she accepts responsibility for the aftercare of the female patient.

Box 13.1: Payment of ordinary fees

Ordinary fees are payable when a GP:

1 accepts a patient, gives contraceptive advice, conducts any examination, prescribes drugs or an occlusive cap and provides follow-up treatment
2 helps to determine the choice of contraception and accepts responsibility for the aftercare

---

Intrauterine device

A GP can claim the intrauterine device fee for services provided to a woman during the 12 month period beginning from the day she applies to have the device fitted. The fee is paid only if the GP, or a partner or an assistant, fits the device and gives all necessary aftercare including any replacement for the next 12 months. It is not possible to claim this fee in addition to the ordinary fee. Twelve months after insertion of the device, the ordinary fee will become payable for any period during which a device is not fitted or replaced. If the device is replaced, the intrauterine device fee becomes payable again for a further 12 months. If the device is replaced within 12 months, this is deemed to be part of the aftercare and no further intrauterine device fee is paid.

Box 13.2: Payment of intrauterine device fee

An intrauterine device fee is payable when a GP fits an intrauterine device and provides aftercare for a period of 12 months

---

Temporary resident patients

A patient who qualifies to be treated as a temporary resident can also be provided with contraceptive services and the GP who accepts such a patient will be paid one-quarter of the annual fee, except that if an intrauterine device is fitted or replaced, the GP receives one-half of the annual intrauterine device fee.

How to claim

Claims should be made on form FP1001 for the ordinary contraceptive fee and on form FP1002 if an intrauterine device has been fitted. Both forms must be signed by the patient and the GP. A claim for a temporary resident patient should be made on form FP1003, and if an intrauterine device has been fitted or replaced the doctor should declare this in Part II of the form.

At the end of 12 months, a new claim must be sent to the FHSA for each patient for whom contraceptive services are continuing. If a patient comes to the surgery for contraceptive services within 1 month of the date on which the 12 month period will end, a new form can be completed and submitted to the FHSA which will accept it as taking effect from the end of the 12 month period. If a patient does not attend at about the time the 12 month period ends but does so within 18 months of the first claim, a GP can still claim that service has been continuous and the FHSA will pay retrospectively for the missing quarters. For instance, if a patient was first accepted in May 1989 but does not attend the surgery again until September 1990 seeking renewal of contraceptive services, the claim can be regarded as being submitted in May 1990. A different doctor can sign the second claim as long as he or she is the successor to the GP making the first claim or both doctors are in partnership.

If a GP accepts a woman for ordinary services but later decides to fit an intrauterine device, a new claim should be made on form FP1002 which will supersede the form FP1001, and a further claim will become due 12 months after the insertion of the intrauterine device.

A GP will cease to be paid for a patient as soon as an FHSA receives a subsequent claim from another doctor. Claim forms should be sent on a regular basis to the FHSA.

Payments

The FHSA calculates the current claims on the first day of each quarter and advises each doctor of the number of patients involved. The GP has 10 days to challenge the figure; if no challenge is made within that time, there will be no other opportunity to do so.

14 Child Health Surveillance Fee

A doctor who wishes to provide child health surveillance and be paid for such services should apply to be included in the FHSA's Child Health Surveillance List.

Eligibility

A doctor on the Child Health Surveillance List will receive a fee for each child under 5 years of age for whom services are provided in accordance with the programme agreed between the FHSA and the District Health Authority (DHA) for the area in which the doctor practises.

Child Health Surveillance Patient List

A doctor on the Child Health Surveillance List should inform the FHSA on form FP/CHS of each child for whom the doctor has undertaken to provide surveillance. The FHSA maintains a list of these children, separate from the normal general medical services patient list. This list may include children on the doctor's normal list together with those on the lists of partners or other doctors with whom he or she works in a group practice.

Level and method of payment

There is one level of fee, and this is paid automatically according to the information provided by the doctor on form FP/CHS as the first day of each quarter. Payment is made whether or not any particular service has been provided in respect of that child during the preceding quarter. Payment will cease once the child reaches the age of 5 years.

15 Minor Surgery

Eligibility

A doctor must be included in the FHSA's Minor Surgery List to claim a fee for undertaking minor surgery. The fee will be payable to a doctor for undertaking minor surgery sessions for his or her own patients or those of partners or group members.

No more than three payments can be made to a doctor in any one quarter. However, if a doctor is a member of a partnership or group, a higher number of payments may be claimed provided that the total number of payments paid in respect of any quarter shall not exceed three times the number of partners or members of the group on the medical list on the first day of the quarter.

What is a session?

A session consists of five surgical procedures. They may be performed either in a single clinic or on separate occasions during the same quarter.

The procedures will count towards a session subject to the following criteria.

1 They are included in the following list:

Injections	intra articular
	peri articular
	varicose veins
	haemorrhoids
Aspirations	joints
	cysts
	bursae
	hydrocele
Incisions	abscesses
	cysts
	thrombosed piles
Excisions	sebaceous cysts
	lipoma
	skin lesions for histology
	intradermal naevi, papilloma, dermatofibroma and similar conditions

	warts
	removal of toe nails (partial and complete)
Curette	warts and verrucae
cautery	other skin lesions e.g. molluscum contagiosum
and cryocautery	
Other:	removal of foreign bodies
	nasal cautery

2 They are performed by a doctor included in the FHSA's Minor Surgery List.
3 Any other person assisting in a procedure is suitably trained or experienced for the task.

Minor Surgery List

A doctor who wishes to perform minor surgery should apply to the FHSA for inclusion in the Minor Surgery List. The FHSA will take into account the qualifying criteria set out in the terms of service.

Claims

Claims for payment are made on form FP/MS. This records basic information about the patient's doctor, the doctor carrying out the procedure and the date and type of procedure.

The FHSA will check the validity of claims.

16 Restricted Services and Limited Lists

A doctor admitted to the medical list for the provision of Maternity Medical Services only

A doctor can be included in an FHSA's medical list to provide MMS only and will be entitled to claim fees for the maternity services he or she provides. It may still be possible to claim reimbursement for rent and rates and under the practice staff scheme; individual applications are considered by the FHSA on their merits. The general principle applied is that a doctor who incurs expenses on premises or staff will receive reimbursement so long as the payment can be justified by the volume of NHS work undertaken. An application form REST2 should be sent to the FHSA together with the relevant PREM and PS forms relating to the premises and staff for which reimbursement is being claimed. If the volume of work does not justify payment at the full rate, a lower rate may be paid. A doctor who is building up a practice which provides only maternity medical services will receive special consideration.

The additional payments during sickness scheme will also apply to a doctor providing maternity medical services only, and the definition of the word 'service' in the relevant paragraph of the Red Book includes service providing maternity services only.

A woman doctor wishing to apply for additional payments during confinement should submit her application via the FHSA to the Secretary of State for Health.

A doctor can also be paid for providing a dispensing service to patients in accordance with the rural dispensing arrangements.

A doctor admitted to the medical list for the provision of Contraceptive Services only

A doctor may be admitted to the medical list to provide contraceptive services only and will be paid the appropriate contraceptive services fees.

Similar provisions to those referred to above, in the section on the provision of MMS only, apply to rent and rates and practice staff reimbursements and additional payments during sickness and confinement.

Payments may be made for the supply of contraceptive drugs and appliances.

A practitioner with a limited list

A doctor whose list is limited to the staff of one or more hospitals or a similar institution in which he or she is employed, or to patients registered in, or connected with, one or more schools or other institutions, is not entitled to a BPA or any of the additions to the BPA. He or she will not be able to claim a postgraduate education allowance or many direct payments for expenses.

However, a limited list doctor is entitled to receive standard capitation fees (including the higher fees for elderly patients) which will be abated by 10%, and if he or she is included in the Child Health Surveillance list, the appropriate fees for Child Health Surveillance will be paid.

The limited list GP is also able to claim fees for special services by submitting the appropriate forms to the FHSA, although a night visit fee will not be paid for any visit to a resident in an institution in which the claiming doctor resides.

A GP with a limited list may be entitled to rent and rates and practice staff reimbursements, and should submit claims to the FHSA. As a general principle, payments will be determined according to the volume of NHS work the doctor undertakes, and may not be at the full rate. The Secretary of State has the final decision about these payments.

A doctor with a limited list in partnership with other doctors providing unrestricted services whose rent and rates and practice staff reimbursements may have to be abated because of that doctor's private income, will receive special consideration from the FHSA.

Additonal payments during sickness may also be paid. A doctor with a limited list of at least 1200 patients will qualify in full for additional payments during sickness. If he or she has less than 1200 patients, the payment will be scaled down to a minimum of a 20% payment for 400 patients. No payment will be made if there are less than 400 patients on the list.

Claims for additional payments during confinement should be sent to the FHSA, which will seek a decision from the Secretary of State.

Practitioners relieved before 1 April 1990 of the liability to provide certain services

A doctor who was permitted by an FHSA's Allocation Joint Committee to be relieved of the responsibility to have patients assigned to him or her under the allocation scheme will continue to receive standard capitation fees, deprivation payments and child health surveillance fees in full but the basic practice allowance will be reduced by 25%.

A doctor who has contracted to provide services for his or her patients out of hours and obtained the consent of the Allocation Joint Committee to be exempted from liability to answer emergency calls during those hours from patients who:

1 are not on his or her list; or
2 are not temporary residents for whom he or she is responsible; or
3 have not been accepted by him or her for the provision of maternity medical services,

will have the basic practice allowance reduced by 5%.

A doctor admitted to the medical list solely to treat patients as temporary residents

A doctor may be included in the medical list solely to treat temporary resident patients at the rates and on the conditions authorized by the Secretary of State. No other payments or reimbursments will be made.

A doctor admitted to the medical list for the provision of Child Health Surveillance Services only

A doctor may be admitted to the medical list to provide only child health surveillance services, and will receive CHS fees only.

Arrangements for reimbursing the costs of premises and staff are similar to those mentioned in this chapter relating to doctors providing MMS Contraceptive Services only.

Additional payments during sickness and confinement may also be claimed.

A doctor admitted to the medical list for the provision of Minor Surgery Services only

A GP can apply for admission to an FHSA's Minor Surgery List and be paid for undertaking minor surgery work. He or she can claim help towards the cost of premises and staff, but cannot receive payments during sickness or confinement. Claims can also be made for the provision of drugs and appliances.

17 Registration Fee

Eligibility

A doctor who carries out the examination procedures specified in the terms of service within 3 months of accepting the patient onto the doctor's personal list will be eligible for a registration fee.

If the examination procedure is carried out more than 3 months after the date of the patient's acceptance, the FHSA will still pay a fee if it is satisfied that the doctor carried out the procedure as soon as possible, and had made all reasonable efforts to do so within 3 months of the patient's acceptance but was prevented by factors beyond his or her control.

However, no fee is paid for:

1 a child under 5 years of age at the time of joining the list;
2 a patient who immediately before joining the list was a patient of a partner, and who participated in a 'registration' consultation during the 12 months prior to the date of acceptance;
3 an examination carried out more than 12 months after the patient's acceptance onto the doctor's list.

Method of payment

Claims should be submitted to the FHSA on form FP/RF. The FHSA may check with patients that registration checks have been carried out.

18 Health Promotion Clinics

Eligibility

A doctor is eligible for a fee for a health promotion clinic provided for patients on his or her list or on the list of a partner or another member of a group practice.

Eligible clinics

The FHSA may decide which clinics qualify for payment. The following guidelines have been provided.

1 Health promotion and illness prevention includes initial surveillance for disease, disability and other health problems and general advice and counselling on the maintenance of good health and well being by the adoption of a healthy life-style. Those clinics which generally qualify for payment are listed in Box 18.1. Other clinics may also qualify.

> **Box 18.1: Health promotion clinics which generally qualify for payment**
> 1 well-person
> 2 anti-smoking
> 3 alcohol control
> 4 diet
> 5 exercise counselling
> 6 stress management
> 7 heart disease prevention
> 8 diabetes

2 A clinic may cover more than one area but if it does only one fee is paid.
3 Provision of day-care facilities does not qualify for a fee.
4 Clinics held wholly or primarily for activities which are already separately remunerated – for example maternity medical services – will *not* qualify for payment.
5 A clinic should normally last at least 1 hour, be advertised to patients in the local directory or practice leaflet, and be provided with separate appointments or with an open appointment system or in a group session. Normally a doctor will be expected to deal with at least 10 patients during a clinic but the FHSA may accept a lower number if it believes that

it is the most appropriate way of providing a service to a group of fewer than 10 patients. Otherwise the FHSA will not authorize a fee if patient attendance regularly falls below 10 or the clinic is unlikely to attract 10 patients.

6 If a doctor is uncertain whether a clinic attracts a fee, the FHSA should be consulted.

Claims

A doctor should claim payment on form FP/HPC and will need to supply this information about the clinic:

1 its title
2 its purpose
3 its date and time
4 the numbers of patients attending.

FHSAs will check the authenticity of claims. Only one doctor will be eligible for payment for each clinic.

19 Night Visit Fees and Out of Hours Services

Night visit fees

A GP is paid a fee for each visit both requested and made between 10 p.m. and 8 a.m. to a patient on his or her personal list, a temporary resident, or a woman for whom he or she is providing maternity medical services who is visited in connection with those services. Both the request and the visit must be made between 10 p.m. and 8 a.m.

Under the pre-1990 GP contract claims were only payable for visits both requested and made between 11 p.m. and 7 a.m.

Claims are made on form FP81. Although the patient's signature is not required on the form, the FHSA will make random checks with patients or their relatives to ensure the validity of claims. If a GP considers there are circumstances that an FHSA should be aware of before it makes a request for confirmation, these should be stated on the form.

Box 19.1: Night visit fees

Paid if:

1 the visit is both requested and made between 10 p.m. and 8 a.m.
2 the patient is on the GP's personal list, or is a temporary resident, or has been accepted for maternity medical services

---

In certain circumstances a claim can be made for treatment given at a surgery or GP hospital, if this was in the patient's interests. A fee may also be paid for a visit to a woman in hospital to provide maternity medical services.

Level of fees

Under the 1990 contract night visit fees are paid at two levels.

A higher fee is payable if the visit is made by:

1 the practitioner with whom the patient is registered; or
2 a partner or member of his or her group practice; or
3 an approved assistant of the partnership or group; or
4 a deputy or locum who is directly employed by a member of the partnership or group and whose employment has been notified to the FHSA under the terms of service, but not where the deputy or locum

made the visit on behalf of a deputizing service with whom such a member had entered into an arrangement approved under the terms of service; or
5 a trainee practitioner employed by a member of the partnership or group, who has completed at least 3 months' training in general practice; or
6 a single-handed practitioner or a practitioner in a group or partnership who is part of a local non-commercial rota which includes practitioners, outside of his or her group or partnership, who may themselves be single-handed, partners or working in a group, whose number does not exceed 10 and who have agreed to provide out of hours cover for each other.

In all other cases a lower fee will be paid.

Box 19.2: Level of fees

The 1990 contract provides two levels of fee for night visits.

A higher fee is paid for visits by the GP with whom the patient is registered, a partner, group member, assistant, deputy, locum, trainee with at least 3 months' general practice experience, or a member of a non-commercial rota of less than 10 practitioners.

In defining 'ten practitioner rotas', the Red Book states that the practitioners need not all work from the same main surgery, and specifies rules about how the practitioners must notify the FHSA of the names of members of the rota. A practitioner may not be in more than one rota at a time.

If more than one patient is seen on a visit to one location, payment is made in accordance with the following formula:

1 two patients seen on 1 visit to 1 location: 1 full fee for each patient
2 additional 1, 2 or 3 patients: one half for each additional patient
3 for each patient seen after the first 5: one tenth of the full fee.

A school, hotel, holiday camp or similar establishment is regarded as one location. If a GP considers that this formula does not provide fair compensation, details should be submitted to the FHSA, which may pay at a higher rate no greater than one full fee per patient.

Practitioners relieved of the responsibility to provide out of hours services

Certain practitioners are relieved of the responsibility to provide out of hours services to their patients under a preserved right specified in paragraph 15(2) of the terms of service. Those who had such relief as at 31 March 1990 will continue to enjoy that relief for as long as they remain on the medical list. Practitioners who assume responsibility out of hours for the patients of these 'opted out' doctors receive a capitation addition for each such patient.

20 Temporary Residents

A GP who treats a temporary resident is paid a higher or lower fee subject to the following conditions:

1 the lower rate is paid if the temporary resident expects to remain in the district for not more than 15 days from the date on which the GP first provides treatment;
2 the higher rate is paid if the temporary resident expects to remain in the district for more than 15 days.

Payment will be made only if an FHSA is satisifed that treatment has actually been provided. A patient is regarded as a temporary resident if he or she is in the area for more than 24 hours but less than 3 months.

Box 20.1: Temporary residents

1 Claims can be made only if treatment is actually provided
2 One of two rates of payment will apply, depending on whether the patient is in the area for less or more than 15 days from the date on which treatment is first provided
3 The patient will be temporarily resident in the area for more than 24 hours and less than 3 months

---

Where the only treatment provided attracts an item-of-service fee for vaccination, immunization, contraceptive services, maternity medical services or the arrest of dental haemorrhage, only the fee for that item is payable and not the temporary resident fee. A night visit can be claimed in some circumstances, in addition to the temporary resident fee. It should be remembered that fees are payable only if the patient is temporarily resident in the area; fees cannot be claimed for patients who are permanently resident in the area but whom a GP wishes to accept only on a temporary basis.

21 Fees for Various Treatments

Emergency treatment

Conditions for payment

A GP can claim an emergency treatment fee for providing a service in an accident or other emergency to a person who is not registered with the practice and who is staying in the area for no more than 24 hours. A fee under this section and not a temporary resident fee will be payable where the person receiving treatment is resident in the area for a period not exceeding 24 hours. It is the total and not the remaining length of stay that determines which claim is made.

To illustrate, if someone is staying in the practice area for only 7 days and needs treatment on the sixth day of the stay, a temporary resident fee is paid and not an emergency treatment fee, even if the patient is returning home within 24 hours of the consultation.

If the service involves a visit between 10 p.m. and 8 a.m., a higher emergency treatment fee is paid. A night visit claim on form FP81 should not be submitted.

Box 21.1: Emergency treatment fees

1 A fee is paid if a GP provides a service to a person who is not registered with the practice and whose total length of stay is less than 24 hours
2 A higher rate is applicable if a visit is made between 10 p.m. and 8 a.m.

Different services attract different levels of emergency treatment fee. In cases where the GP considers that a service not defined in the list in paragraph 1, schedule 1 of the Red Book has been provided, or an abnormal amount of time has been taken in providing the treatment, an application for a special fee can be made, setting out full details of the case. The FHSA may then recommend the Secretary of State to authorize a special fee.

If a GP provides a service to a patient of a neighbouring practice, the FHSA may deduct the payment (except the fee for a visit made between 10 p.m. and 8 a.m.) from the patient's own doctor if the doctor was not available to provide the service personally. Before doing so, the FHSA will give the doctor the opportunity to explain the non-attendance.

The FHSA will not pay an emergency treatment fee for a service for which it is possible to claim a fee under the Road Traffic Act unless satisfied the GP has been unable to recover that fee. The fee is usually paid through the motor vehicle insurance company. The FHSA can be asked for advice concerning the action a GP should take in order to obtain payment from the insurance company and asked whether an emergency treatment fee will be paid if the payment cannot be recovered.

When the service provided by the GP attracts a payment under the vaccination and immunization scheme, or involves the arrest of a dental haemorrhage, then an emergency treatment fee is not payable.

Form FP73 should be used for a vaccination, and form FP82 for the arrest of a dental haemorrhage.

How to claim

Form FP32 should be sent to the FHSA, and should include details of any appropriate Rural Practice Claim.

The flow chart set out in Fig. 21.1 indicates the circumstances in which a temporary resident fee, an emergency treatment fee or a fee for immediately necessary treatment can be claimed.

Immediately necessary treatment

Conditions for payment

If a person applies for treatment and the GP is unwilling to accept him or her as a patient or a temporary resident but the person requires treatment, the GP is obliged under the terms of service to provide all immediately necessary treatment. A fee is payable for this service, and may be claimed on form FP106.

The GP will be paid a fee for the service at the same rate as would be received for a temporary resident, even if the patient is assigned to his or her list within 3 months of the date the service is given.

However, if the person is accepted as a permanent or temporary resident patient by the doctor or the doctor's partner within 3 months, the GP will be deemed to have accepted the patient on the date that the immediately necessary treatment was provided.

If a night visit fee is also appropriate in addition to the immediately necessary treatment fee, a claim may be submitted to the FHSA.

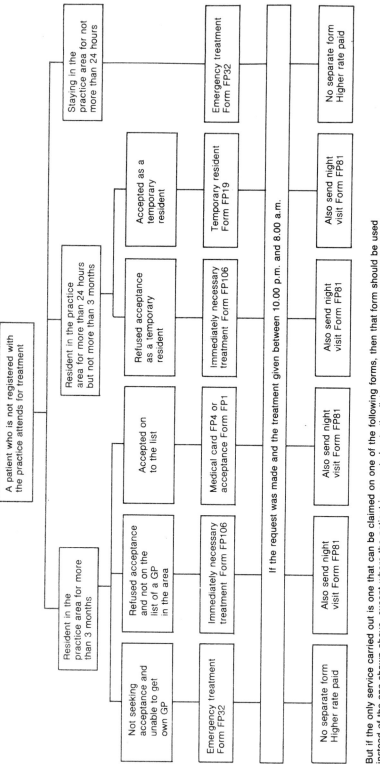

A patient who is not registered with the practice attends for treatment

Resident in the practice area for more than 3 months

- Not seeking acceptance and unable to get own GP
  - Emergency treatment Form FP32
    - No separate form Higher rate paid

- Refused acceptance and not on the list of a GP in the area
  - Immediately necessary treatment Form FP106
    - Also send night visit Form FP81

- Accepted on to the list
  - Medical card FP4 or acceptance Form FP1
    - Also send night visit Form FP81

Resident in the practice area for more than 24 hours but not more than 3 months

- Refused acceptance as a temporary resident
  - Immediately necessary treatment Form FP106
    - Also send night visit Form FP81

- Accepted as a temporary resident
  - Temporary resident Form FP19
    - Also send night visit Form FP81

Staying in the practice area for not more than 24 hours

- Emergency treatment Form FP32
  - No separate form Higher rate paid

If the request was made and the treatment given between 10.00 p.m. and 8.00 a.m.

But if the only service carried out is one that can be claimed on one of the following forms, then that form should be used instead of the one shown above, except where the patient is accepted onto the list:

Vaccination   FP73   Contraceptive services   FP1003
Arrest of dental haemorrhage FP82
Maternity Medical Services   FP24

Figure 21.1.

Arrest of a dental haemorrhage

Conditions for payment

A GP who treats a patient for the arrest of a dental haemorrhage, or provides aftercare relating to the arrest of a dental haemorrhage, such as the removal of a plug or stitches, can claim a fee for this service on form FP82. However, a GP who arrests the haemorrhage, or his or her partner or assistant, cannot also be paid for the administration of aftercare.

If a night visit fee is claimed for attending a patient in need of the arrest of a dental haemorrhage, a fee for arresting the haemorrhage will **not** be paid in addition.

Service of an anaesthetist

Conditions for payment

A fee is payable to a GP when the services of a second doctor are required for the administration of a general anaesthetic for any reason other than in connection with maternity services, in which case a fee is payable under the maternity services section of the Red Book.

The fee is payable when the anaesthetic is administered by the GP responsible for the patient or by the second doctor, although a fee cannot be claimed if the anaethetic is administered by a trainee or by a doctor who is administering the anesthetic for the operation to be performed by a trainee. A fee is not payable if the operation at which the anaesthetic is given is performed under the arrangements made by the hospital services.

If a practice is likely to submit more than 65 claims in a quarter, the FHSA will submit details to the Secretary of State, who will decide on the appropriate fee.

How to claim

Claims should be submitted to the FHSA on form FP31.

22 Target Payments

Cervical cytology

As part of the new contractual arrangements GPs will no longer be paid individually for cervical cytology tests. Instead, payment is to be based on a system of target payments based on specified levels of uptake.

Eligibility

A GP will receive a target payment at the higher rate if, on the first day of each quarter, at least 80% of the eligible women on his or her list, aged between 25 and 64 (21 and 60 in Scotland), have had an adequate smear (taken by any source) during a period of 5.5 years preceding the claim. Women aged 25 to 64 are defined as being those born between the second day of the same quarter 65 years earlier and the first day of the quarter 40 years later. For example, on 1 October 1990, the target population of women includes those born between 2 October 1925 and 1 October 1965.

A GP will be paid a target payment at the lower rate if at least 50% of the eligible women on his or her list have had an adequate test.

When the scheme was initially proposed, target payments were to be individual to the doctor concerned, relating solely to the women registered on his or her list. The scheme has now been modified so that target payments may be calculated on a partnership basis.

The actual payment requires further calculations. It depends on the number of eligible patients, compared with those on the list of the average GP, and the number of adequate smears taken as part of general medical services as opposed to those done at DHA or private clinics.

The system of paying individual claims for cervical cytology ceased on 31 March 1990, although a claim for a test taken up to that date will be met by the FHSA if it is made within 6 months of the smear being taken. The FHSA has discretion to accept later claims made before 1 April 1991.

Who is excluded from the target calculation?

Women who have had hysterectomies involving the complete removal of the cervix are excluded from the total number of women on the list for calculation of the coverage level. GPs need to notify their FHSA of the number of women in the age group who have had hysterectomies, and the number of those women who have had an adequate smear in the preceding 5.5 years, and to inform it of new cases. No other categories of women are excluded from the calculation.

Maximum sum payable

The maximum sum payable to a GP depends on the number of eligible women aged between 25 and 64 on his or her list, compared with the number of eligible women in the same age group on the list of the average practitioner. In the 1990 SFA the average practitioner is deemed to have 430 eligible women, and therefore the maximum sum payable to an individual GP is calculated as follows:

$$\frac{\text{eligible number of women on GP's list}}{430} \times \begin{array}{c} \text{maximum sum payable} \\ \text{to the average GP.} \end{array}$$

Calculating the payment

The GP is eligible for the whole of the appropriate maximum payment if at least 80%, or 50% as appropriate, of the eligible women have had adequate smear tests carried out by GPs as part of general medical services.

The smear test may have been undertaken by other doctors in the partnership or other GPs, for example if the woman was registered with another GP before joining the current GP's list. As long as the tests were adequate and taken under general medical services, they are counted.

When only a proportion of the adequate smears are done as part of general medical services and others are done elsewhere, the maximum payment will be scaled down accordingly. This applies in all other situations, including when tests are taken by a GP as part of work for which payment by a health authority or another source is received.

If any smears are repeated during the 5.5 year period, an adequate smear taken by a GP will take precedence over one taken by any other source for the purpose of calculating payments.

Examples

The following two examples help to explain the target calculation and payment system.

Example 1

Target calculations

Total number of eligible women aged 25 – 64
(hysterectomies excluded)   = 360

Total number of women who have had an adequate smear
in the preceding 5.5 years   = 300

$\frac{300}{360} = 83.3\%$

Higher target payment is achieved. The number of smears required to reach the higher target (the target number) is 288 (80% of 360).

Calculation of maximum sum payable

$$\text{Maximum sum payable} = \frac{360\ (\text{Eligible number of women on GP's list})}{430\ (\text{Eligible number of women on average list})} \times \begin{array}{c} \text{Maximum sum payable} \\ \text{for the average} \\ \text{practitioner (80\% level)} \end{array}$$

Calculation of payment

Total number of adequate smears = 300
of which 200 done by GP or partner
          40 done by another GP
          50 done by DHA
          10 done privately

Therefore 240 were undertaken under general medical services.

$$\text{Maximum sum payable} \times \frac{240}{288} = \text{actual payment}$$

Example 2

Target calculation

Total number of eligible women aged 25 – 64
(hysterectomies excluded)   = 200

Total number of women who have had an adequate smear
in the preceding 5.5 years   = 110

$$\frac{110}{200} = 55\%$$

Lower target payment is achieved. The number of smears required to reach the lower target (the target number) is 100 (50% of 200).

Calculation of maximum sum payable

$$\text{Maximum sum payable} = \frac{200}{430} \times \begin{array}{c} \text{maximum sum payable for} \\ \text{the average practitioner} \\ \text{(50\% level)} \end{array}$$

Calculation of payment

Total number of adequate smears = 110
of which 80 done by GP or partner
        15 done by another GP
        10 done by DHA
         5 done privately
Therefore 95 were undertaken under General Medical Services.

Maximum sum payable $\times \dfrac{95}{100}$ = actual payment

Further information about payments

It is expected that by April 1994 all FHSAs will have sufficient data on their computer systems to calculate entitlement to payments based on their own information.

Until then, or until an FHSA's records are completely up to date, the FHSA will have discretion to apportion tests whose origins are unclear in proportion with the known proportion of tests carried out by a GP for women on his or her list. For instance, if the source of 12 tests is unclear and a GP has been responsible for taking the tests of 150 women of his or her eligible list of 192, then $\dfrac{150}{180} \times 12$, i.e. 10, of the unclear source tests will be allowed for payment.

An FHSA will also accept until 1994 information based on a GP's own records, and form FP/TCC should be used to make the appropriate claim if a doctor believes from the evidence of the practice records that a target has been reached.

The authenticity of the entitlement may be checked by the FHSA.

So that GPs receive a full year's payments in the first year of the scheme's operation, those providing general medical services on 1 April 1990 will be paid twice their entitlement for the first quarter of the 1990–91 year on 30 September 1990.

Immunization for children aged 2 and under

The new contractural arrangements provide for a target payment system to replace the previous arrangement of individual payments for each immunization provided to children under the age of 2.

Eligibility

A GP will be eligible for a target payment at the higher rate if, on the first day of a quarter, the number of courses completed in each of the following groups of immunizations amounts on average to 90% of the number of courses needed to achieve full immunization of all children aged 2 on his or her list. For the purpose of calculation, children aged 2 are defined as children born between the second day of the same quarter 3 years earlier and the first day of the corresponding quarter 1 year later, inclusive. For example, on 1 October 1990, the larger population of children includes those born between 2 October 1987 and 1 October 1988.

Group one		Group two	Group three	
Diphtheria			Measles	
Tetanus	3 doses	Pertussis 3 doses	OR	
Poliomyelitis			Measles	
			Mumps	3 doses
			Rubella	

A GP will be eligible for a target payment at the lower rate if the average of courses completed amounts to 70% of the number needed for full immunization.

When the scheme was first proposed, entitlement to the payment was to be based on an individual practitioner's list. The scheme has now been modified so that target payments may be assessed on a partnership basis.

Maximum sum payable

The maximum sum payable depends on the number of children aged 2 on the GP's list, compared with the number of children aged 2 on the average practitioner's list. In the 1990 Red Book, the average practitioner is deemed to have 22 patients of this age on his or her list. Therefore, a GP with 30 children aged 2 or under on the list would be entitled to

$$\frac{30}{22} \times \text{the maximum sum payable to the average GP.}$$

Calculating the payment

The proportion of the payment due to the GP depends on the number of courses of immunization completed by doctors as part of general medical services as opposed to those completed elsewhere, for example at health authority clinics.

A course completed by other GPs, inside or outside the partnership, as part of general medical services will count towards the payment of the doctor making the claim. This means that if a child who has had all the completing doses moves from another part of the country and registers with a new doctor, the new doctor will be able to count that child towards the target payment even though none of the immunizations were provided personally.

A course will be considered as being completed by a GP as part of general medical services if he or she gives the final immunization needed to complete cover for the diseases in that group. For instance, in group one the completing immunization will be the third poliomyelitis, provided that the child has also had 3 doses of diphtheria and tetanus vaccine.

Method of calculation

First it is necessary to decide how many completing immunizations are needed to reach a target. Twenty children have 60 immunization groups. So to reach the 70% target, 42 completing immunizations would be required, and for the 90% target, 54 would be needed. If the calculation results in a fraction, the target will be rounded to the nearest integer (0.5 being rounded down).

Secondly, it is necessary to decide whether a target has been reached, by adding the numbers of completing immunizations carried out in each of the three groups. Thus, completing immunizations in excess of the target number in one group can top up the number in another group.

Thirdly, if a target has been achieved, it is necessary to calculate the maximum sum payable, comparing the actual number of eligible children with the number on an average GP's list.

Fourthly, it is necessary to count the number of completing immunizations carried out by GPs as part of general medical services for the three immunization groups, so that the appropriate proportion of the maximum sum payable can be calculated. Only one completing immunization per child can be counted for each group. Where the number of completing immunizations in each group done by GPs as part of general medical services is greater that the number of children needed to reach the target level, the latter figure is counted. For example, if a GP has 10 children on his or her list aged 2, 8 have completed their immunizations in each of the three groups, and all the completing doses were given by GPs, then the 70% target has been reached. As the 70% target number is 7 children who have had completing immunizations, only 7 count towards the work done by GPs in each group. Therefore, the number of completing immunizations done by GPs is regarded as $7 + 7 + 7 = 21$ (= 100% of the number needed to reach the 70% target).

Finally, the actual amount payable is then calculated by multiplying the maximum sum payable by the number of completing immunizations done as part of general medical services for the three groups added together and dividing by the number necessary to achieve the appropriate percentage cover. As there are three groups, the number necessary to achieve the target is the appropriate percentage of three times the number of children concerned.

If a GP works for another organization such as a health authority, then any immunization carried out as part of the contract will not be counted for payment.

Immunizations done before 1 April 1990 for which an item-of-service fee was payable are counted for target payments. Work done by employed or attached staff at the direction of a GP as part of general medical services is also counted for payment.

Records and claims

Claims should be made on form PT/TC1 no later than 4 months after the date to which the claim relates.

To ensure that a full year's payment is made during the first year of operation of the scheme, GPs will be paid twice their entitlement for the first quarter of that year on 30 September 1990.

GPs should report details of all immunizations to the appropriate health authorities, and also inform the FHSA of any appointments they hold with health authorities which involve childhood immunizations.

Example

At the end of the quarter a GP has 20 children on his or her list aged 2. Of these, all 20 have had complete courses of immunizations against diphtheria, tetanus and poliomyelitis. Ten of the completing immunizations were given by the GP's own practice, 5 by another GP practice and 5 by a DHA clinic.

Fifteen of the children have had complete courses of immunization against pertussis. Of these 8 were given by the GP's own practice, none by another GP practice and 7 by a DHA clinic.

Twelve of the children have been immunized against measles, mumps and rubella. Of these courses, 5 were given by the GP's own practice, 2 by another GP practice and 5 by a DHA clinic.

Step one: How many completing immunizations are needed to reach a target?

Twenty children have a maximum of 60 completing immunizations.
The 70% target requires 42 completing immunizations.
The 90% target requires 54 completing immunizations.

Step two: Has a target been reached?

Group 1 (DT and P)	20
Group 2 (Pertussis)	15
Group 3 (MMR)	12
Total	47

The 70% target has been reached.

Step three: What is the maximum sum payable?

$$\frac{20}{22} \times \begin{array}{l}\text{maximum sum payable to the}\\ \text{practitioner with an average list}\end{array} = \text{maximum sum payable}$$

Step four: What proportion of the work needed to reach the target was done by GPs as part of general medical services?

Group 1	GP's own practice	10
	Another GP	5
	Total	15

but since 70% = 14 immunizations, this is treated as 14

Group 2	GP's own practice	8
	Another GP	0
	Total	8
Group 3	GP's own practice	5
	Another GP	2
	Total	7

	Group 1	14
	Group 2	8
	Group 3	7
	Total of completing doses regarded as carried out by GPs	29

Step 5: How much is the payment?

Number of completing immunizations regarded as given by GPs = 29
Number of completing immunizations needed to reach 70%   = 42

Payment = $\frac{29}{42}$ × maximum sum payable for 70% target

Pre-school boosters for children aged 5 and under

Just as target payments have been introduced for immunization of children aged 2 and under, they are also payable for pre-school boosters for children aged 5 and under.

Eligibility

A GP is eligible for a target payment at the higher rate if, on the first day of each quarter, 90% of the children on his or her list who are aged 5 had had reinforcing doses of diphtheria, tetanus and polio immunizations. Children aged 5 are defined as those born between the second day of the same quarter 6 years earlier and the first day of the quarter a year later. For example, on 1 October 1990, the target population of children includes those born between 2 October 1984 and 1 October 1985.

If 70% of the children under 5 have reinforcing doses then a target payment at the lower rate will be made. The payment to be made will depend on the number of eligible patients, compared with those on the list of an average GP, and on the number of boosters given by GPs as opposed to those given by others. A child will only be considered as fully immunized if he or she has received booster doses of all three vaccines. One or two vaccines will not count.

Maximum sum payable

The number of children on a GP's list aged 5 compared to the list of an average GP will determine the maximum sum payable. If a GP actually has 30 children on his or her list then the maximum sum payable is calculated as follows:

$$\frac{30}{22} \times \text{maximum sum payable to the average GP.}$$

Calculating the payment

The amount payable depends on the level of cover achieved and the number of complete booster doses of immunizations given by GPs as part of general medical services. Those provided by other sources, for example health authority clinics, do not count. Boosters given by other GPs under general medical services — for example if a child is given the necessary boosters by a GP in one practice and then moves to another part of the country and registers with a new doctor – will be counted in the target calculation of the claiming GP. The child will be counted towards the new GP's target levels and not those of the doctor who gave the boosters.

The first step in working out the payment to be made is to decide whether 90% or 70% of the total number of children have received booster doses for all three vaccines. In calculating the 90% or 70% target number, fractions will be rounded to the nearest integer (0.5 being rounded down). If a child does not have all three boosters at the same time, no account will be taken of them until all three boosters have been given. The booster will count as having been given by whoever gave the third booster dose.

Secondly, if a target is reached, the number of booster doses given as part of general medical services is counted so that the appropriate proportion of the maximum sum payable can be calculated.

Thirdly, the actual amount is calculated by multiplying the maximum sum payable by the number of booster doses given under general medical services, and dividing by the number of boosters necessary to achieve the appropriate percentage cover.

Work does not count as having been performed by a GP as part of general medical services if he or she immunizes children under a paid contract outside of general medical services. Immunizations done before 1 April 1990 for which an item-of-service fee was paid will be counted, as will work done by employed staff or attached staff under the direction of a GP.

Records and claims

Claims should be made to the FHSA on form FP/TPB no later than 4 months after the date on which eligibility is assessed. GPs will be paid twice their entitlement for the first quarter of 1990–91 on 30 September 1990 so that they can receive a full year's payment during that year.

GPs are responsible for reporting all immunizations to the appropriate health authority as ɔon as they are given. This allows health authorities to provide GPs with information to help them in claiming payments.

GPs are also responsible for reporting to the FHSA any appointment that a GP holds with a health authority which includes the carrying out of pre-school boosters.

23 Vaccinations and Immunizations

IN addition to the target payment system for the vaccination and immunization of children, a doctor (or a doctor's deputy) who vaccinates a patient in accordance with public policy is able to claim a fee for the service, provided that the patient is on the GP's or his or her partner's list, or is eligible for treatment as a temporary resident or is staying in the area for less than 24 hours.

If the vaccination is given by a suitably qualified person employed by the GP or staff attached to the GP's practice and who work at his or her direction, it will be regarded as having been provided by the GP and a fee will be payable.

Doctors who are paid to vaccinate patients by District or Port Health Authorities will not be able to claim a fee under this paragraph.

Box 23.1: Fee for vaccination

This fee is payable if:

1 the vaccination is in accordance with public policy
2 the patient is registered with the practice, a temporary resident, or staying in the area for less than 24 hours

---

In local outbreaks of disease any emergency programmes of vaccination are under the direction of the appropriate authorities. The vaccination given by a doctor during an outbreak will qualify for a payment if it is not given during a session for which the doctor is employed by the health authority and if the person vaccinated is a member of a group for which vaccination has been recommended by the local community physician, or the person has been in close contact with a person suffering from the disease and the vaccination is subsequently approved by the community physician, or the vaccination qualifies for an item-of-service payment in any case.

How to claim

Claims for payment should be made on form FP73. Both parts of the form should be completed and sent to the FHSA, which will detach part 2 and send it to the health authority. Details of the diseases, the groups of persons affected for whom fees are payable and details of the fees are set out in schedule 1 to paragraph 27 of the Statement of Fees and Allowances.

24 Supply of Drugs and Appliances

GPs can claim payment for supplying drugs and appliances to their patients in two ways.

1 Where these have been supplied and personally administered by prescribing or dispensing doctors to any patient. This is restricted to vaccines, anaesthetics, injections, diagnostic reagents, intrauterine devices, contraceptive caps and diaphragms, pessaries which are appliances, and sutures (including skin closure strips).
2 Where these have been supplied by dispensing GPs to patients on their dispensing lists or to temporary residents staying in dispensing areas.

Payment for the drugs and appliances includes:

1 the basic price less any discount calculated in accordance with the Statement of Fees and Allowances;
2 an on-cost allowance of a percentage of the basic price *before* deduction of any discount;
3 a container allowance for each prescription;
4 a dispensing fee;
5 an allowance in respect of VAT (this allowance is payable only to those GPs who have not registered with HM Customs and Excise for VAT purposes);
6 exceptional expenses as provided for in the Drug Tariff.

Payments for the supply of oxygen and oxygen therapy equipment are not covered by the above and are not subject to the discount arrangements.

A dispensing doctor who, with a patient's consent, issues a prescription form to enable him or her to obtain drugs or appliances from a pharmacist is not entitled to any remuneration under this part of the Red Book. Where a doctor, or a partnership of doctors, is able to provide evidence to the FHSA that because of the remoteness of the practice they cannot obtain any discount on the basic price of drugs and appliances, the FHSA may exempt the practice from the application of the discount scale. FHSAs have the right to grant exemption for periods up to one year, and these may be renewed provided that the practice is able to satisfy the FHSA that it is still experiencing difficulty in obtaining discount.

Where a doctor or a partnership of doctors can show the FHSA that, because of the remoteness of the practice or the small quantities of drugs and appliances they buy, they obtain their supplies at a price on average more than 5% above the basic price, the FHSA can approve a special payment to remunerate the practice at a rate in excess of the basic price of the drugs. Details are set out in paragraph 44.8 of the Red Book.

Claims

All prescriptions from both dispensing and prescribing doctors should be noted, counted and sent under the cover of form FP34D to the Prescription Pricing Authority. Prescriptions should be sent no later than the fifth day of the month (for example, prescriptions relating to items supplied to patients during July should be sent by 5 August). GPs should ensure that endorsement of the prescriptions in the appropriate column follows the instructions in paragraph 44.9 of the Red Book.

GPs in partnership should submit all prescriptions for pricing in one batch under the cover of one claim form for the entire partnership so that the appropriate discount rates may be applied. For calculation of the dispensing fee, doctors may if they wish subdivide the partnership batch into bundles relating to individual GPs, provided that the bundles are joined together in one partnership batch.

Any doctor who wishes to examine his or her priced prescription forms should contact the FHSA which will arrange to obtain the forms from the Prescription Pricing Authority.

Prescription charges

Items supplied by either dispensing or prescribing doctors under the arrangements for personally administered items do not attract prescription charges and therefore no charge should be made to the patient.

Accounting

To ensure that the Inland Revenue's annual survey of doctors' practice expenses is carried out accurately, GPs should ensure that their actual expenditure on drugs and appliances (i.e. the amounts paid to their suppliers) is shown 'gross' in their accounts. Similarly, payments received for supplying drugs and appliances should be brought to account 'gross' as 'income' in exactly the same way as other fees and allowances received from the FHSA.

Oxygen therapy services

The Drug Tariff sets out the conditions for payment for the supply of oxygen and oxygen therapy equipment and relates to both pharmacists and dispensing doctors. The Red Book explains how dispensing doctors are paid and includes the appropriate amendments to take account of the fact that a dispensing doctor and not a pharmacist is providing this service. Dispensing doctors providing this service receive a fixed annual rental payable in monthly instalments for each oxygen set or stand that they are authorized to hold by the FHSA, irrespective of whether the equipment is on loan to a patient. Any dispensing doctor who wishes to be authorized to hold oxygen equipment, or to increase the number of sets or stands he or she is authorized to hold, should apply to the FHSA. Details of the method of claiming together with the rates that are applicable are set out in paragraph 44 schedule 3 of the Red Book.

25 Undergraduate Medical Students

IF a GP assists a recognized university department of general practice in the teaching of medical students by giving them experience in general practice, he or she will be paid according to the number of students involved and the time they spend in the practice.

The students should be from a recognized university department of general practice in the UK and the medical school should have arranged the training with the GP. It will be necessary for the university to confirm that the training has taken place.

A GP who satisfies these conditions may claim a fee for each session that the student is attached to the practice.

Time spent in the practice will relate to education and training in general medical services, including observation and instruction in the work done by all members of the practice team.

A session will consist of at least 2.5 hours of such activity in any 24 hour period. No more than two sessions per student may be claimed for any 24 hour period.

Only one GP may claim in respect of any time spent by a student in a practice during any 24 hour period. This should normally be the GP with whom the medical school has arranged the attachment.

Box 25.1: Undergraduate medical students

1 A GP may claim sessional fees for teaching undergraduate medical students.
2 Each session consists of at least 2.5 hours of teaching activity.
3 No more than two sessions will be payable for each student in any 24 hour period.

Claims should be made on form FP/UMS, and should set out details of the number of sessions claimed for and of the time spent in the practice by each student. A GP should also send with the claim written confirmation from the university that the students were attached to the practice at the times and dates shown on the claim form. GPs will be responsible for obtaining this written confirmation.

It will help the local FHSA if GPs inform it of the details of the university departments with which each GP is linked for teaching undergraduate medical students.

26 The Trainee Practitioner Scheme

Becoming a trainer

THE approval of trainers in training practices is the responsibility of the General Practice Sub-Committee (the Sub-Committee) of the Regional Postgraduate Education Committee. Any GP wishing to apply or reapply to be a trainer should do so directly to the Sub-Committee, the address of which can be obtained from the FHSA or the Regional Health Authority.

A panel appointed by the Sub-Committee interviews the applicant and arranges to visit the applicant's surgery before giving approval.

A GP will be approved as a trainer initially for a period not exceeding 2 years; further extensions can be given for periods of up to 5 years. If there is any change in a trainer's circumstances or practice, the Sub-Committee may review, suspend, vary or terminate its approval.

If a GP applies to be a trainer and is dissatisfied with the decision of the Sub-Committee or is aggrieved by a decision affecting his or her appointment as a trainer, an appeal may be made to a national Appeals Committee within 28 days of receiving the Sub-Committee's decision. Details of how to appeal are set out in paragraphs 38.3 and 38.4 of the Red Book.

Conditions for payment

Any GP whose name is included in an FHSA's medical list and who has been approved as a trainer is entitled to payments while a trainee is working in the practice.

It is important that the trainer should always tell the FHSA when a new appointment is made. Any delay in notifying the FHSA will delay payment.

Training periods are usually for 12 months whole-time (or the equivalent part-time). This period includes holidays which should not exceed 5 weeks plus public and bank holidays. Training may be split between two practices: for example 6 months may be spent with one trainer and 6 months with another.

The trainer's grant cannot be paid for more than 12 months in respect of the same trainee unless the training period is extended. If the arrangements between the trainer and the trainee are terminated early, both the Sub-Committee and the FHSA should be told. There are certain circumstances in which a doctor may not need to undertake a full 12 month period of training; details of these are set out in paragraph 38.5(a) i, ii and iii of the Red Book.

If a trainer's appointment has less than a year to run, a new trainee should not be engaged without applying to the Sub-Committee. A trainer will normally be entitled to payment for only one trainee at a time, but payments for the salary of an additional trainee may be authorized if an overlap of training is appropriate and is authorized by the Regional Postgraduate Dean. An additional training grant is not paid in these circumstances.

A trainer must tell the FHSA and the Sub-Committee if there are any material changes to the conditions of his or her practice, including a reduction in the amount of time any assistant works in the practice.

A GP should normally have a list of at least 2000 patients (or 1500 in rural areas) to be a trainer. Smaller lists may be acceptable but will require the approval of the Sub-Committee.

A trainer is responsible for appointing a trainee and should not pay any salary in excess of the amount approved by the FHSA. Trainees cannot be included in any medical list.

If a doctor has been appointed as a vocational scheme course organizer, he or she will not also be expected to assume responsibility for an individual trainee, although a trainer's grant will still be paid for work as a course organizer.

Types of payment

A trainer receives the following payments when a trainee is in the practice.

1 A training grant.
2 Reimbursement of the employer's share of the national insurance contributions paid in respect of the trainee. (The trainee pays the employee's share.)
3 A motor vehicle allowance, according to the type of vehicle, if an additional motor vehicle is necessary in the practice for the trainee.
4 The costs of installing an extra telephone extension at the surgery and a new telephone at the trainee's residence.
5 The cost of the rental charge for a telephone at the trainee's residence (provided that the trainee is responsible for the rental charge), and the cost of installation and the rental charge for a bedroom telephone extension at the trainee's home provided that the FHSA is satisfied that the extension is necessary to enable the trainee to perform his or her duties satisfactorily and the trainer confirms that this is so.
6 The trainee's salary, which relates to the basic salary the trainee was paid in his or her last regular NHS hospital post. Details of how salary is calculated, and of any increases applicable during the 12-month period, are set out in paragraph 38.6(e) of the Red Book.

The FHSA will give advice on how much should be paid, but it is essential that the FHSA is informed as soon as an appointment is made so that it can obtain information from the trainee's previous employer, in order to determine the salary to be paid in good time to make reimbursement at the appropriate rate.

7 If the trainer requires the trainee to be a member of a medical defence organization, the FHSA will reimburse the trainee's subscription or premium costs, less the costs which would have been incurred if the trainee had taken out the basic subscription ('additional cover') payable by hospital doctors.

Removal expenses of doctors becoming trainees in general practice

A doctor who leaves a post with an NHS authority to take up an appointment as a trainee in general practice or moves from one training practice to another and, as a result, changes accommodation can claim removal expenses, but only if the FHSA is satisfied that removal of the trainee's home is necessary. The payments made are broadly similar to those made to hospital doctors under Section 26 of the NHS General Whitley Council Conditions of Service Handbook. A trainee should seek an acceptance from his or her FHSA that removal is necessary and that removal expenses will be payable before incurring any expenditure. In considering the application, the FHSA may examine the location of the trainer's practice area in relation to the trainee's existing home and the road links to the practice area.

Short unavoidable breaks in service due to unemployment or a locum appointment between leaving one post and taking up the general practice training post may be disregarded by the FHSA.

The FHSA will also decide whether the proposed move is reasonable. A reasonable arrangement is defined as a move to accommodation which is broadly comparable to that already occupied by the trainee. Where there is a demonstrable improvement in the standard of accommodation, the FHSA will relate payment of expenses to a notional purchase price or rent assessed by a local estate agent based on a property which is broadly comparable with the trainee's existing home but related to prices in the new area. If an improvement in accommodation is apparent, the FHSA will make proportional payments connected with the cost of purchase of property or rent in the new location and the notional price or rent will be used instead of the actual costs. The intention of this arrangement is that the move should cost the FHSA the same amount of money as if the trainee had moved to a house of identical standard. For instance, if a trainee leaves a two-bedroom semi-detached house which is sold for £50 000 and buys a four-bedroom house in the new area for £95 000, the FHSA may ask a local estate agent to assess the likely cost of the two-bedroom house in the new area. If the old property is assessed as being worth £65 000 in the new area, the FHSA will apportion the reimbursement of the costs involved in the purchase, such as solicitor's fees, by 65/95. If a trainee was compulsorily resident in Health Authority accommodation the FHSA has discretion to determine what is broadly comparable accommodation in the new area having regard to the standard of accommodation which the trainee may have had to accept in previous employment.

Throughout the conditions for payment, reference is made to a house-holder, which is interpreted as being a trainee who, in the area of previous employment, occupied unfurnished accommodation of more than two rooms either rented or owner occupied, although the FHSA can ask the Secretary of State to vary this definition in cases of hardship.

Expenses of removal, house purchase and sale

Removal

Before removal of the trainee's furniture and effects, the FHSA should approve the cost. When furniture is being removed by contractors, three competitive tenders should be obtained and sent to the FHSA. A trainee is able to accept a tender other than the lowest, but the FHSA will base reimbursement on the lowest tender. Tenders should be subject to the usual conditions of removal and should not cover special services such as relaying of carpets or taking down or putting up of fixtures.

The expenditure that will be reimbursed is the cost of the removal of furniture and effects belonging to the trainee and the dependant members of his or her household from the old home to the new. This will include pedal cycles and heavy but ordinary items of gardening equipment or furniture, but items such as grand pianos which involve special arrangements will be excluded. Livestock other than domestic pets must be conveyed at the trainee's own expense.

Reimbursement can also be made of the cost of removal from the old home to storage and then to the new home. Where housing difficulties make it necessary, payment will be made of the cost of transferring such articles as cots, perambulators, radio, television and high-fidelity equipment to temporary accommodation in furnished rooms while transferring the majority of furniture to storage.

Storage

If it is necessary to store articles of furniture and effects reimbursement will be made of the cost of storage. If a trainee is unable to find suitable accommodation and has to store some furniture while occupying temporary unfurnished accommodation in the new area, he or she will be reimbursed storage charges only when the rent in the new area exceeds that of the old, otherwise payment will be restricted to the amount by which the rent in the new accommodation plus the storage charges exceeds the old rent.

Insurance on furniture in transit will be allowed up to the value for which it is ordinarily insured by the trainee. Extra insurance charges on stored furniture will be treated as part of storage charges.

Legal and estate agent fees

A householder may claim reimbursement for all reasonable legal and other expenses (including VAT) when because of the traineeship a house is purchased and it is the first permanent unfurnished accommodation that is occupied in the area of the training practice or a house is sold immediately before taking up the traineeship. The removal must be for more than 6 months and receipts and vouchers to prove the expenditure must be produced. It will be helpful for the FHSA to have estate agents' details of the properties that are being bought and sold, if estate agents have been used. Such expenses in connection with house purchase may include solicitors' fees, stamp duty, land registration fees, incidental legal expenses, expenses in connection with a mortgage or loan including guarantee and survey fees, the cost of a private survey, an electrical wiring test and a drains test. If a trainee incurs expenses relating to a proposed purchase which is abandoned, the FHSA may make reimbursement of those costs provided that they are reasonable in relation to the work done. The FHSA will have to be satisfied that the trainee was in no way responsible for the abandonment or that the reasons for withdrawing from the sale were reasonable.

Relating to house sale, the reimbursable costs are solicitors' fees, including legal expenses incurred in mortgage redemption, and house agents' or auctioneers' fees. If a trainee chooses to sell the house him- or herself without involving an estate agent, he or she may claim incidental expenses up to a set limit for telephone calls, advertising and postage.

No compensation can be paid for any loss on the sale of a house consequent on taking up a traineeship.

If a trainee lets his or her house instead of selling, the legal expenses relating to the letting may be reimbursed. However, the trainee will not be entitled to legal expenses in connection with a subsequent sale.

A trainee who obtains a bridging loan will be reimbursed interest charges (net after tax relief). The amount will relate to a loan not exceeding the estimated selling price of the old house and will continue for up to 3 months providing that the FHSA is satisfied that the trainee acted reasonably in arranging to buy a house before selling the existing property. Reimbursement of interest may continue beyond 3 months as long as the FHSA is convinced that the trainee is making every effort to sell at a reasonable figure.

Tenancy

Within a defined limit, the costs of a tenancy agreement, house agents' fees and a drains test can be reimbursed to a trainee who chooses to rent furnished accommodation. These expenses are not reimbursed to trainees who move into rented lodgings.

Travelling expenses

Preliminary visit

A trainee may claim travelling and subsistence expenses for visiting the new area of traineeship in order to search for accommodation. The amounts payable will be at the same rate as those payable for attending educational courses and subsistence will not be paid for more than four nights. A trainee who takes his wife with him will receive additional subsistence for the same period at two-thirds of the rate paid to trainees. Any children aged 12 years or over also accompanying the trainee will attract a subsistence payment of two-thirds and any child under 12 years can be claimed for at half the trainee's rate.

Journey from the old home to the new

The cost of one journey (and if the length of journey warrants it, subsistence allowance) will be paid in respect of the trainee and dependants. In this context, the dependants will include any person under 21 years who moves to the new home with the trainee even though he or she may be earning his or her own living. The term dependant also includes one servant or nurse.

Return visit to superintend the removal

If a trainee returns home to superintend the removal, travelling expenses will be paid for the purpose. Subsistence allowances may also be paid as long as the number of nights when added to the period of the preliminary visit does not exceed four. Subsistence is not payable when the trainee uses or could use the old accommodation or stays with relatives.

Loss of season tickets

A trainee may claim for the unexpired value of a railway or bus season ticket, provided that the amount is irrecoverable from the railway or bus company, but reimbursement will relate only to the quarter current at the time of removal.

Losses arising from educational arrangements

Details of the amounts and conditions relating to claims for losses arising from educational arrangements are set out in paragraph 38.11(e) of the Statement of Fees and Allowances. An allowance may be claimed where the move results in a loss of school fees paid in the old area, or towards the lodging costs of a child who has to be left in the old area for educational reasons.

Allowance during search for accommodation

Subsistence

A married trainee (or a single trainee with equivalent responsibilities) who does not find suitable accommodation before taking up the traineeship and leaves the family at home may claim night subsistence equivalent to that payable for training courses. This amount will be payable provided the FHSA is satisfied that the trainee is making every effort to find suitable family accommodation.

Visits home

Subsistence allowances will continue even if the trainee returns home to the old area at weekends provided that he or she is away from lodgings for not more than three nights. Travelling expenses will be reimbursed at weekly intervals for visits home.

Excess daily travel

A trainee who is able to travel daily to the area of traineeship whilst looking for suitable family accommodation may be reimbursed the extra cost incurred in travelling on the basis of bus fares, second class rail fares, or travel by private motor vehicle. The reimbursement will not exceed the long-term subsistence rate and will continue only as long as the FHSA is satisfied that the trainee is actively seeking suitable family accommodation.

Miscellaneous expenses grant

A miscellaneous removals expenses grant, as set out in paragraph 43 of Section 26 of the General Whitley Council Conditions of Service Handbook, is payable to a trainee as compensation for the additional expenses of occupying new permanent accommodation. The amount will be payable in full to those trainees who have not made a similar claim during the previous 2 years. A trainee who has made a similar claim will have expenses limited to the actual expenditure incurred and reimbursement will be conditional on him or her submitting a statement of expenditure to the FHSA. In paragraph 38.12(e), some examples of the type of expenditure that would qualify, such as installation of a television aerial, plumbing in a washing machine and redirection of mail, are defined.

Continuing commitments allowance

If a trainee incurs expenditure on rent and rates in the new area while also incurring similar expenditure in the old area, an allowance will be made to offset the costs.

1 Married trainees or those with equivalent domestic commitments will be paid an allowance equal to the continuing commitments in the old area or the long-term night subsistence allowance, whichever is the less, for up to 3 months from the date the family join the trainee in the new area.
2 Single householders will be paid a similar allowance for up to 3 months from the date of taking up the traineeship.
3 Single trainees will be paid whichever is the less of the continuing commitment in the old area or the retention of rooms allowance set out in paragraph 38.14, again for a period of up to 3 months from taking up the traineeship.

If any part of the accommodation in the old area is let, the rent received will be deducted from any amount payable. The allowance will not be paid when a trainee is receiving bridging loan expenses as set out in paragraph 38.10.

Retention of rooms allowance

If a trainee is temporarily absent from lodgings in the area of the traineeship (for instance at weekends) but has to pay in order to retain the rooms, he or she will be able to claim an allowance unless a night subsistence allowance for weekend periods of absence is being paid.

Payment of rent of unoccupied property

If a trainee has to commence payment of rent on a property to secure a property in the area of traineeship while still paying rent in the old area, he or she may be reimbursed up to the amount of the long-term night subsistence rate.

Payment of travelling expenses and additional accommodation costs in lieu of removal expenses

If a trainee establishes a permanent home in order to undertake his or her vocational training and chooses to travel from home to the location of the various posts he or she holds during the period of the training rather than move, excess daily travelling expenses can be claimed. In other words, if the trainee lives 3 miles from a hospital at which he or she holds a hospital post and chooses to travel 23 miles when he or she moves into general practice, the trainee will be entitled to claim for 20 miles per journey by way of excess travelling, provided that the FHSA is satisfied that removal expenses would have been appropriate if the trainee had chosen to move.

A trainee may choose to take temporary lodgings away from his or her permanent home and close to the training practice, in which case actual expenses may be paid.

Payment of expenses of trainees when on call

A trainee who qualifies to receive payments under the above two paragraphs and is required by the practice to be on-call may stay in lodgings close to the practice on those nights and weekends when on-call. On such occasions, the trainee will not qualify for excess daily travelling but will receive reimbursement of the actual lodging expenses, limited to the long-term night subsistence rate.

Excess rent allowance

The arrangements for excess rent allowance are set out in Section 26 of the General Whitley Council Conditions of Service Handbook. The allowance is meant to compensate a trainee who moves to a more expensive area in order to take up a traineeship and will relate to either owner-occupied or rented accommodation. Full details of the scheme are set out in paragraphs 38.18 to 38.23 of the Red Book. Trainees are advised to seek advice from their FHSA about the complex arrangements for payments.

Interview expenses

A trainee who attends for an interview with a trainer in connection with a possible traineeship will receive reimbursement of travelling and subsistence expenses unless the application is withdrawn or the offer of appointment is refused.

Payments to trainees during sickness

If a trainee is sick and absent from the practice for up to 2 weeks, payments will continue to the trainer but will be abated by the amount of Statutory Sick Pay (SSP) received. It will not usually be necessary to extend the traineeship in those circumstances. Where a trainee is absent for more than 2 weeks, payments will continue for reimbursement of the national insurance contributions and the salary of the trainee for periods of up to 3 months, again abated by SSP, and when SSP ceases by sickness or injury benefits payable under the National Insurance Act. Payments for the training grant and the car allowance will cease during the period of sickness. The Secretary of State has discretion to extend payments for absences in excess of 3 months and application should be made via the FHSA. The traineeship may be extended to allow for completion of training. Trainers should inform the FHSA when their trainee is unable to work because of sickness.

Maternity leave for trainees

Payment of the trainee's salary will continue to be made during maternity leave taken if the conditions set out in paragraphs 38.29 to 38.42 of the Red Book are met.

Payments of expenses involved in sitting examinations for postgraduate qualifications

A trainee who sits an examination for a postgraduate qualification may be paid travelling and subsistence allowances, at the rates paid when attending approved educational activities. No claim can be made for an examination fee or the cost of typing or binding papers for the examining body. The trainee should send the claim form (GPCF3) to the FHSA, with confirmation by the trainer that the trainee attended the examination.

27 The Doctors' Retainer Scheme

THIS scheme is for doctors who work not more than one day a week and who wish to remain in touch with medicine so that they can return to a fuller commitment to the NHS when their circumstances permit. They have the opportunity to do a small amount of specially arranged paid professional work and to attend postgraduate medical education sessions, and they receive a small retainer to help meet their expenses. The scheme is primarily intended to help women doctors but there is no obstacle to the inclusion of men.

The scheme is administered by the Regional Health Authority together with clinical tutors working under the auspices of Postgraduate Deans and Regional Postgraduate Medical Committees.

The scheme requires a doctor to work at least one half-day per month and be ready to take on sessional work up to a maximum of one day per week, provided this does not conflict with family commitments.

If the doctor wishes, these service sessions may be in a general practice approved by the Regional Postgraduate Education Committee. The doctor works as an assistant in the practice. The time worked is a matter to be agreed by the doctor, the practice and the clinical tutor, and the terms of employment are to be agreed between the doctor and the practice.

The FHSA will reimburse a practice which employs a retainer scheme doctor up to a maximum of the fee for a notional half-day per week. A notional half-day is defined as 3.5 hours, and subject to the maximum of one half-day per week, a practice can agree with the FHSA how many sessions are claimed for.

Box 27.1: Doctors' retainer scheme

The FHSA will reimburse the employing practice for a maximum of one notional half-day per week

---

Information about the scheme can be obtained from the Regional Adviser in General Practice.

28 Postgraduate Education Allowance

Eligibility

A practitioner will be paid an allowance if he or she:

1 has attended 25 days of accredited postgraduate education spread reasonably over the 5 years preceding the claim; and
2 has during that time attended at least two accredited courses in each of the following three subjects:

> health promotion and the prevention of illness
> disease management
> service management.

Each doctor in a job-sharing arrangement is eligible for payment of the allowance if he or she individually satisfies the criteria in this chapter.

Courses which qualify

Courses are accredited if approved, in England by the Regional Adviser on Postgraduate Education, or in Wales by the Postgraduate Dean in consultation with his or her associate adviser as appropriate. Those organizing courses therefore need to apply for this approval to obtain accreditation.

The Regional Adviser will determine the number of days accreditation for a course, and the subject areas into which the sessions of the course fall. The three subject areas listed above cover the following:

'Health promotion and the prevention of illness' includes the promotion of healthy living and the prevention of disease, injury and ill health.

'Disease management' includes the natural history of disease and injury and treatment and care of the sick and terminally ill.

'Service management' includes aspects of providing efficient care to patients including data and record systems, the use of technology and of staff and health care teams, practice organizations cost effective prescribing, quality assurance and audit and the interface between different caring services.

A course may include a period of formal education or informal education, for example at a GP's surgery, and may run continuously for a specific period or consist of separate sessions held regularly and frequently in a single subject area.

Distance learning

Distance learning packages may be accredited by the Regional Adviser, according to their educational value. In accepting a package, the Regional Adviser will determine a notional length in terms of qualifying days.

Unpaid clinical attachments

Unpaid clinical attachments under consultant supervision and (normally) supernumerary to establishment may be accredited by a Regional Adviser. In such a case the Adviser will determine the subject area into which it falls, and the notional length of the attachment in terms of qualifying half-days.

Doctors teaching on courses

A doctor teaching at an accredited course will be considered to have attended that course for half a day. If the course lasts for more than half a day and the doctor attends the full course, he or she will be credited with attendance as for all other practitioners. If the doctor teaches during sessions covering more than half a day in total, he or she will be considered as having attended for those sessions.

Doctors becoming GPs for the first time more than 12 months after completing vocational training

A doctor joining the list more than 12 months after completing vocational training will be paid the full allowance if the following conditions are satisfied:

1 the first claim is within 12 months of becoming a GP; and
2 each subsequent claim is made within 15 months of the preceding claim; and
3 **first claim:** the doctor has attended at least 5 days of accredited postgraduate educational courses within the year preceding the claim;
   second claim: the doctor has attended at least 10 days of accredited postgraduate education in the 2 years preceding the claim, including at least one course accredited as being in each of two subject areas;
   third claim: the doctor has attended at least 15 days of accredited postgraduate education courses reasonably spread over the 3 years preceding the claim including at least one course accredited as being in each of the three subject areas;
   fourth claim: the doctor has attended at least 20 days of accredited postgraduate education courses spread reasonably across the 4 years preceding the claim, including at least one course accredited as being in each of the three subject areas.

Doctors becoming GPs for the first time within 12 months of completing vocational training

A doctor will be paid the full allowance for the four quarters preceding the claim provided the first claim is made within 12 months of completing vocational training.

Subsequently, provided each claim is made within 15 months of the preceding claim, the doctor will be paid the full allowance if the following conditions are met:

second-first subsequent-claim: the doctor has attended at least 5 days of accredited postgraduate education courses during the year preceding the claim;

third claim: the doctor has attended at least 10 days of accredited postgraduate education courses in the 2 years preceding the claim, including at least one course accredited as being in each of two subject areas;

fourth claim: the doctor has attended at least 15 days of accredited postgraduate education courses over the 3 years preceding the claim, including at least one course accredited as being in each of the three subject areas;

fifth claim: the doctor has attended at least 20 days of accredited postgraduate education courses over the 4 years preceding the claim, including at least one course accredited as being in each of the three subject areas.

What happens if a GP fails to maintain the 5 year programme?

If a GP is unable to qualify for the full allowance, he or she will be eligible for a reduced allowance subject to the following conditions:

Level 1 can be claimed if a doctor has attended at least 5 days of accredited postgraduate education courses in the 5 years preceding the claim;

Level 2 can be claimed if a doctor has attended at least 10 days of accredited postgraduate education courses in the 5 years preceding the claim, including at least one course accredited as being in each of two subject areas;

Level 3 can be claimed if a doctor has attended at least 15 days of accredited postgraduate education courses over the 5 years preceding the claim, including at least one course accredited as being in each of the three subject areas;

Level 4 can be claimed if a doctor has attended at least 20 days of accredited postgraduate education courses over the 5 years preceding the claim, including at least one course accredited as being in each of the three subject areas.

Claims

Form FP/PEA is used to claim payment. Claims can be made at any date following the completion of courses, and the allowance will be paid for the following 12 month period. No new claim can normally be made within 12 months of the date of the previous claim. The FHSA will require documentary proof of course attendance.

It should be noted that an FHSA may withhold payment of all or part of an allowance if it considers that a course has been unreasonably repeated, or that the days are spread unreasonably between years. A GP is not expected to claim for more than 10 days in any year.

Arrangements during 1990

A doctor is eligible for the full allowance if by April 1990 he or she has attended 5 days of accredited education in the preceding year.

A doctor who does not satisfy this requirement may still claim the allowance by 1 October 1990 if he or she has completed 5 days of accredited education in the period from 1 April 1989, and will be considered to have been eligible for the allowance on 1 April 1990. The doctor may make the next claim after 1 April 1991.

Doctors who qualify for the full allowance will be eligible for full payment in subsequent years provided the following criteria are met:

1 each **subsequent claim** is made within 15 months of the preceding claim; and
2 **second claim** (after 1 April 1991): the doctor has attended at least 10 days of accredited postgraduate education courses in the 2 years preceding the claim including at least one course in each of two of the subject areas;
3 **third claim:** the doctor has attended at least 15 days of accredited postgraduate education courses spread over the 3 years preceding the claim, including at least one course accredited as being in each of the three subject areas;
4 **fourth claim:** the doctor has attended at least 20 days of accredited postgraduate education courses spread over 4 years preceding the claim, including at least one course accredited as being in each of the three subject areas.

Courses held between 1 April 1989 and 31 March 1990 will be considered as accredited if they were:

1 approved under Section 63; or
2 an individual clinical attachment, under consultant supervision and normally supernumerary to establishment.

The Regional Adviser will determine the length and subject group of such courses and advise the FHSA.

29 Reimbursement of Rent and Rates

Eligibility

A GP is eligible to be paid under this scheme if his or her list of patients is at least 100. If a doctor who has a list of less than 100 patients is building it up, the FHSA may agree reimbursement.

Acceptance of premises

Purpose of the scheme

The scheme aims to reimbuse GPs the cost of rent and rates on practice accommodation by taking account of what each doctor pays or is deemed to pay.

Alternatively, GPs may purpose-build surgery accommodation or substantially alter existing accommodation and be reimbursed a cost rent. This scheme is explained on pages 135 to 146.

As the scheme significantly reduces an individual GP's financial interest in the expense incurred, the FHSA has to be satisfied that the use of the existing premises or the enlargement of premises is in the interests of the NHS.

Move of premises

The FHSA must ensure that premises and their use are reasonable, and it will therefore assess any proposed move. If a move or a proposed enlargement of surgery premises would unreasonably increase payments under the scheme without improving the service to NHS patients, an FHSA will not increase reimbursement beyond that already being paid. For example, the FHSA, LMC and District Health Authority may have agreed to make future provision for general medical services in a development or redevelopment area through the planning of a health centre.

In such circumstances, the FHSA would not accept 'new' practice premises under the scheme in that area because these would be contrary to its plans.

Similarly, a GP may want to move from a health centre and provide his or her own surgery premises. Unless the FHSA is satisfied that there are good reasons for doing so, it will not increase reimbursement beyond the 'notional' figures already paid for the health centre.

New branch surgeries

Payments for new branch surgeries are limited to the size of accommodation which the FHSA regards as reasonable for NHS patients in the area.

Similarly, where a doctor wishes to provide new outlying consultation facilities in a rural area, the FHSA will need to be satisfied that the population in the area is best served by this arrangement before accepting the proposal.

Consultation with the FHSA about proposed changes in surgery accommodation

Since payments under the scheme are only made if accommodation is accepted by the FHSA, GPs must consult the FHSA *in advance* on proposed changes to their premises. Otherwise:

1 the FHSA may not accept that the changes improve services to patients;
2 the GP may not receive an increased notional rent or may be unaware of other schemes that may help to improve premises.

What should doctors do if they are unhappy with an FHSA decision about surgery premises?

If a GP disagrees with an FHSA's decision on accepting premises or enlarging existing or proposed premises, representations should be made to the Secretary of State for Health within 2 months of the FHSA's decision. The GP must state the reasons for dissatisfaction with the FHSA decision.

What is the FHSA looking for when accepting surgery premises under the scheme?

The scheme applies to premises shown in the medical list where GPs see NHS patients at advertized open surgery sessions and by appointment. The FHSA has to be satified that reasonable use is made of premises; *those used for occasional consultations will not be accepted under the scheme.*

Premises may be either a separate unit or part of a residence, and may be rented or owned by a GP or a close relative of the GP. A close relative is defined as the spouse of the doctor, or son, daughter, parent, grandparent, brother or sister of the doctor or his or her spouse. When premises are owned or rented by a close relative of the GP, they are treated as if they were owned or rented by the GP.

For payment purposes, only those parts of the premises used directly for NHS practice will be accepted. For example, garages and carports will be accepted only if they form part of separate practice premises. Parking space for practitioners used by both the practice and patients is acceptable.

Residential accommodation is not accepted for payment unless it is occupied by someone, other than a GP, who answers patients' calls after surgery hours. Any rent received from an occupant will be taken into account in assessing payments under the scheme.

If the practice accommodation is rented, or is included within premises subject to a rental agreement, the FHSA may wish to see the lease or tenancy agreement. The GP will need to state whether he or she or a member of his or her family is related to or in any way connected with the lessor, including a private company of which he or she or any of his or her partners or a member of his, her or their families is a member.

With the exception of certain premises in rural areas, main or branch surgery accommodation will not be accepted under the scheme unless the FHSA, following a visit, is satisfied that the following criteria are met:

1 ease of access to premises and movement within them, bearing in mind the needs of the elderly and disabled people, including those in wheelchairs, and mothers with young children;
2 a properly equipped treatment room is provided, and a properly equipped consulting room, with adequate arrangements to ensure the privacy of consultations and patients' personal privacy when dressing or undressing, either in a separate examination room or in a screened off area around an examination couch within the consulting or treatment room;
3 the GP, staff and patients to have convenient access, including wheelchair access, to adequate lavatory and washing facilities (GPs should have a wash basin in or immediately adjacent to their consulting room);
4 adequate internal waiting areas with enough seating to meet all normal requirements, and provision, either in the reception area or elsewhere, for patients to communicate confidentially with reception staff, including by telephone;
5 the premises, fittings and furniture to be kept clean and in good repair, with adequate standards of lighting, heating and ventilation;
6 adequate fire precautions, including provision for safe exit from the premises, designed in accordance with the Building Regulations agreed with the local fire authority;
7 adequate security for records, prescription pads, pads of doctors' statements, and drugs;
8 where the premises are used for minor surgery, a suitable room and equipment for the procedures for which the room and equipment are used.

Clearly, accommodation in premises in a rural area normally used for other purposes cannot always satisfy these criteria; nevertheless, there must be adequate facilities for consulting patients.

FHSAs routinely visit premises, and if they find surgery accommodation which does not comply with these standards, rent and rates reimbursement may be abated or withheld. They must give 6 months' notice of their intention, and GPs can appeal to the Secretary of State against such a decision.

FHSAs may also ask Medical Service Committees to investigate the acceptability of a GP's surgery accommodation under paragraph 24 of the terms of service.

Payments

FHSAs calculate reimbursements of rent and rates on accepted premises as follows.

Rents

1 Cost rents for new separate purpose-built accommodation or its equivalent (*see* pages 135 to 146).
2 Notional rents for owner-occupiers, for separate premises or premises forming part of a residence.
3 Payments for rented separate premises, for premises in rented residences or for premises rented from local authorities which charge an economic rent.

How are notional rents and payments for rented premises determined?

Notional rents and payments for rented premises are determined after the current market rent has been assessed by the District Valuer (DV).

What is the current market rent?

Current market rent is the rent which the District Valuer considers might reasonably be expected to be paid for the premises at the time of valuation.

Rates

1 General rates.
2 Water rates.
3 Sewerage, miscellaneous, environmental, drainage or embankment rates.

Rates will not be reimbursed separately if the rental of the premises includes rates.

Water meter supply

Water authorities may now offer GPs the option of paying for the water supply to practice premises on a metered basis instead of through a charge calculated on the rateable value of the premises.

It is in the interests of the NHS that any savings realizable by a change to a metered supply should be obtained; FHSAs will encourage doctors to change to a metered system when savings can be achieved.

Therefore, if it can be shown that a change to a metered system may produce savings in comparison with continued reimbursements of water rates, and that the annual savings may be sufficient to cover the historic cost of installing a water meter within 4 years, the installation costs and meter charges will be directly reimbursed irrespective of whether the expected savings are achieved. Water authorities can advise GPs on the likely costs involved.

Refuse collection charges

If a local authority levies a separate charge for collecting trade refuse from surgeries, or where suitable alternative arrangements exist, for instance arrangements made by health authorities or private contractors for which there is a charge, the lowest charge levied may be reimbursed if receipts are submitted.

Box 29.1: Rent and rates scheme payments

1 Cost rents
2 Notional rents
3 Rental reimbursements
4 General rates
5 Water rates
6 Sewerage, etc., rates
7 Water meter installation costs and charges
8 Refuse collection charge reimbursements

Abatement of payments

Abatement of payments on account of private income

If a doctor earns private income from work conducted at or associated with premises accepted under the scheme, payments will be abated if the gross income from this work is at least 10% of total gross income. Private income includes all professional income received from other than public sources.

An abatement of 10% is made if 10% but less than 20% of gross income is from private work, of 20% if over 20% but less than 30% is, and so on.

A GP undertaking private work at a surgery not accepted under the scheme may still have reimbursement on the NHS surgery abated unless he or she can show that the private income was wholly derived from work at the private surgery and that the practice accounts are drawn up in such a way as to identify this income separately.

Use of surgery accommodation by other bodies

If a GP allows accommodation to be used by a DHA or another body or organization, payments under the scheme will be abated by the amount of the rent received by the GP as part of the arrangement.

Separate premises

Under the scheme, separate premises are self-contained premises used only for practice purposes and assessed separately as such for rates.

Payment for rented premises will be the lease rent or the District Valuer's assessment of current market rent, whichever is lower.

In all cases where the rental covers non-practice accommodation, the current market rent will be assessed on the basis described in the Red Book.

If the GP owns the freehold of separate premises or the premises are held under a ground lease by the GP, a notional rent is assessed by the District Valuer at the date of occupation.

If rates are not included in the rent paid under a lease or tenancy agreement, or general rates are paid for premises owned by the GP, these are reimbursed separately. They will be abated according to the division of gross value for rating purposes, as assessed by the District Valuer, if non-practice accommodation is included in the premises.

Practice accommodation in a residence

If the accommodation is in a residence owned by the doctor, notional rent and rates payments are only made for that part of the residence used regularly and substantially for practice purposes.

Some rooms may be used at different times for both domestic and practice purposes; in these cases a part payment is made. For example, a room used regularly for a certain number of hours a day as a waiting area for patients will be accepted for partial payment under the scheme as accommodation in dual use. Similarly, if minimal domestic use is made of part of the surgery accommodation, that part will be accepted as wholly used for practice purposes.

However, if a branch surgery is in a residence and advertized surgery sessions are held on less than 3 days a week, an FHSA will not accept any of the accommodation as being in dual use, and it will not therefore qualify for partial payment under the scheme.

The FHSA determines the notional rent for the practice accommodation on the advice of the District Valuer, who assesses the current market rental value of that part of the premises used for practice purposes.

The gross value for rating purposes of the residence as a whole will be apportioned by the District Valuer according to the details of the accommodation provided by the GP and agreed by the FHSA. The payment in respect of rates will be an amount bearing the same proportion to the actual rates paid on the residence as a whole, as the apportioned gross value for rating bears to the total gross value for rating. For those parts of the accommodation in dual use, payment will be based on the ratio between the apportioned value of the parts used solely for practice purposes and that of the parts used solely for non-practice purposes. Thus, if, in the case of a residence with a gross value for rating of £360, the District Valuer advises that £200 relates to accommodation in sole use for non-practice purposes and £100 relates to accommodation in sole use for practice purposes (i.e. a ratio of 2 to 1), the apportioned gross value for rating the remaining part in dual use would be $£(1/3 \times 60) = £20$.

If the practice accommodation forms part of a residence rented by the GP, payments under the scheme relate solely to that part used regularly and substantially for practice purposes. The rental value and gross value for rating will be apportioned by the District Valuer as described above. The apportioned figures will then be applied to the accepted figures for rent and any separate payment of rates.

Claims for payment and accounting

GPs should ensure that they actually claim reimbursement of rents paid and of rates and water rates. Every FHSA could provide numerous examples of practices which do not claim at all or claim intermittently.

Rent

Claims for payment should be sent to the 'responsible' FHSA. Payments are normally made a quarter in arrears, but if requested to do so an FHSA will make rental payments on a monthly basis. In practice, most FHSAs automatically make payments on a monthly basis unless requested not to do so. Monthly advances will not be made if the rent is paid at greater than monthly intervals, but reimbursement will be made as soon as possible after receipts are submitted.

Rates

Rates will be reimbursed as soon as possible after receipts are submitted to the FHSA.

Claims on form PREM2 should be submitted to the FHSA annually, within 7 days of the end of the quarter ending 30 June.

Details of practice accommodation

When a GP acquires premises, form PREM1 must be completed, giving details of the practice accommodation. The form is completed in triplicate, two copies being sent to the FHSA and one copy being retained by the GP. It is essential that form PREM1 is sent to the FHSA whenever the accommodation or its ownership changes.

As soon as possible after receiving form PREM1, the FHSA will advise the GP whether the premises are accepted under the scheme. If the practice accommodation forms part of a residence, the FHSA will also confirm whether the schedule of accommodation used for practice purposes is acceptable.

A GP will be told what payment will be made by the FHSA as soon as it has received the District Valuer's advice.

It is often necessary for an FHSA officer to visit the practice premises before the FHSA authorizes acceptance of new accommodation or changes, and he or she will often be accompanied by an LMC representative. Almost always, the District Valuer will also need to visit the practice.

What should a GP do if dissatisfied with the payment proposed by the FHSA?

If a GP is not satisfied with the proposed payment or with the apportionment of the gross value for rating where non-practice accommodation is involved, he or she may submit independent evidence to the FHSA for consideration by the District Valuer. If, having done so, the GP is still dissatisfied, representations may be made to the Secretary of State.

Declaration of expenses on rent and rates to the Inland Revenue

To avoid confusion in the Inland Revenue's annual survey of practice expenses, all GPs should ensure that their expenses on rent and rates are shown as gross expenditure in their accounts, and payments made under the scheme are shown as income, in the same way as other income from the FHSA.

Review of payments

Notional rents

For notionally rented premises, the notional rent will be reviewed 3 years after the date of any assessment made on or after 1 October 1976.

When a review is due, the FHSA will send form PREM1 to the GP. The form is usually sent some time before the review date, to enable the GP to complete the form and return it to the FHSA, which will send it on to the District Valuer so that any revised valuation can be reflected in an increased payment as near as possible to the review date.

Some GPs fail to return the form to the FHSA and others only do so after a considerable delay. It is in a GP's interest to return the form as soon as possible.

A minor change in the accommodation may be accepted by the FHSA, but a significant change would normally require a visit to the surgery by an FHSA officer.

The District Valuer may also wish to visit the premises, particularly if the practice accommodation forms part of a residence and there has been a change in the ratio of domestic to practice use.

The District Valuer will be prepared to negotiate with GPs or their professional advisers so as to reach agreement on a current market rent or the apportionment to be recommended to the FHSA.

GPs are notified by the FHSA of the revised payments to be made, and these normally continue for 3 years unless there are changes to the premises or they are no longer used for general medical services.

Accommodation in a residence owned by a doctor

The notional rent is reviewed every 3 years in the same way as notional rents on separate premises.

Rented premises

The assessment of the current market rent of accommodation rented by a GP is related to the period of the lease or rental agreement and is reviewed when the lease or agreement is varied.

Review of rating assessments

Whenever the rating assessment changes, the apportionment of the gross value used to calculate the reimbursement of rates, and of the rent or notional rent of surgeries in residences, is also reviewed.

GPs should tell FHSAs when their rating assessments change, so that the review of the apportionment can be initiated. If doctors are dissatisfied with a revised apportionment, they can make representations to the Secretary of State.

Local Authority economic rents

Under this part of the Rent and Rates Scheme, an FHSA may reimburse an economic rent when this is charged by a Local Authority for practice premises.

Economic rent is defined and the method of calculation described in LASSL(80)3, which is available from the FHSA. It also describes the certification necessary for payments.

The premises must be accepted by the FHSA, and the rules for abatement for private practice are applicable.

Where a GP is provided with temporary accommodation by a Local Authority, he or she may be charged for restoring it to some other use, for instance housing. These costs should not be included in the rent charged, but the liability for charges should be reported to the FHSA when the premises are first occupied, as the doctor may be eligible for assistance in meeting this cost. A claim may be met in full if the FHSA is satisfied that:

1 the work is necessary to restore the surgery to its intended use;
2 the costs of the necessary work are not excessive; and
3 the GP's period of occupation of the premises was not unreasonably short.

30 Improving Surgery Accommodation

What help is available for improving surgery accommodation?

1 Notional rent and rent reimbursement.
2 Improvement grants.
3 Cost rent payments.

Notional rent and rent reimbursement

Minor improvements to surgery premises that do not attract an improvement grant or a cost rent payment will normally attract an increased notional rent.

Improvement grants

General provisions

Grants are available to fund improvements to premises if the FHSA's prior approval has been obtained. It will have to take account of its predetermined priorities and its cash allocation for the relevant period when considering an application. Hence it may happen that an applicant is not offered a grant at all.

GPs may be eligible for grants of between one-third and two-thirds of the cost of the improvements, including the professional fees associated with both the design and the supervision of the work, and the statutory fees charged by a Local Authority for approving plans and inspecting the building.

Grants will not be paid on projects costing less than the figure set out in schedule 2 of the improvement grant section of the Red Book.

Doctors eligible for grants

Grants are available to all GPs providing unrestricted general medical services if their NHS list in the case of a single-handed practice, or their average list in the case of doctors in partnership, contains 500 or more patients (urban areas) or 350 or more (rural areas), or is expected to reach these levels within a year.

Projects eligible for grant

Examples of projects that would qualify under the scheme include the following.

1 Adding new rooms, for example, consulting room, a room for minor surgery, patients' toilet and washing facilities.
2 Bringing into use rooms not previously used.
3 Enlarging existing rooms.
4 Improving the heating system.
5 Extending telephone facilities.
6 Double-glazing.
7 Installing security systems.
8 Installing fire precautions.
9 Car and pram parking.
10 Improving access to premises, including access for those in wheelchairs.

To attract a grant, the work must in the view of the FHSA significantly improve existing practice arrangements. In arriving at that view, the FHSA will take account of the standards it sets for accommodation.

The work must improve on what already exists, rather than result in the provision of new premises whether by new building or by rebuilding. For that reason, the premises to be improved must normally be in current use for NHS practice purposes and must already have been accepted under the Rent and Rates Scheme.

However, premises not previously used for NHS purposes may be accepted for a grant if the FHSA considers that they could have been used for NHS practice in their existing state. There is a maximum grant payable for improving premises in these circumstances.

GPs must have security of tenure: the premises should be owned by the practice or held on a lease at least as long as the minimum period of use specified in the scheme. If premises are leased, the landlord's written approval of the alteration must be sent to the FHSA.

If work is undertaken on premises not used solely for NHS practice, a grant will be paid only in respect of the practice part of the accommodation.

If it is intended to extend existing premises a grant is only paid if:

1 any building separate from the main building is attached by at least a covered passageway;
2 the total area of the accommodation in the completed project does not exceed that specified in the cost rent schedules (*see* page 139).

Projects ineligible for grant

The following costs will not be reimbused by a grant.

1 The initial provision of premises including the costs of acquiring land, existing buildings or new buildings.
2 The replacement or part replacement of premises. This includes projects such as the building of an extension to house part of or all of the practice premises so that the original premises can revert to private use.
3 The provision or replacement of furniture (except when built-in), furnishings, floor covering or equipment.
4 The repair or maintenance of premises, furniture, furnishings, floor covering and equipment.
5 The restoration of structural damage or deterioration.
6 Any work in connection with the domestic part of any accommodation.
7 *Any project where a contract has been entered into, or work commenced, without the FHSA's prior approval.*
8 *Any expenses on which a tax allowance is being claimed (see page 135).*
9 That part of an extension which, together with the original practice accommodation remaining in use after the new work has been carried out, exceeds the area allowed under the cost rent schedules.
10 Any extension not attached to the main building by at least a covered passageway.

Apportionment of total cost where premises are used for other purposes

If a project includes expenditure not attributable to the medical practice, a division of costs is necessary. An apportionment may also be necessary if the premises are used for a substantial amount of private practice.

Guarantee of continued use after improvement

Before grants are paid, doctors have to sign an undertaking that the premises will continue to be used for NHS practice for a minimum period specified in the scheme and that, if required, they will repay a proportion of the grant should they fail to observe this undertaking.

How to apply for a grant

GPs should seek advice from the FHSA and its medical adviser at an early stage, as this can frequently prevent unnecessary design work and expense.

An application form should be returned to the FHSA with the following documentation.

1   Estimate of total costs, including fees, prepared by a builder, architect, surveyor or other suitably qualified person.
2   Sketch plan of the existing premises, showing the size and present use of rooms.
3   Sketch plans of the proposed work.
4   A specification of the work to be done.
(NB: If the cost is over a specified figure, the above documents must be prepared by an architect, surveyor or other suitably qualified person.)
5   *Either* a statement from the Local Authority confirming that there is no obstacle to the project in its development plans, building regulations or by-laws *or* copies of documents giving the relevant approvals.
6   If the property is leased, the landlord's written consent to the alterations.
No application will be considered by an FHSA without this documentation.

How the FHSA proceeds

If the FHSA decides that a doctor's proposals are a significant improvement on what exists, it will decide what priority to give the scheme, bearing in mind its forward programme for surgery improvements.

If a scheme is 'approved in principle' the applicant will be informed, and advised of the proportion of grant which will be paid and of any conditions concerning the target date or target timeband when the proposed payment is to be made. This should enable the doctor to decide whether to proceed with the scheme or to modify it. The GP needs to advise the FHSA in writing of this decision, and then should obtain tenders for the approved project. Normally, 3 are required and the grant is based on the lowest tender.

The FHSA will give approval for the work to start and ask the GP to complete an agreement form. *No part of the grant can be paid until this agreement is completed.*

If a GP finds that variations to the scheme are necessary, the FHSA should be informed immediately.

Where a project is estimated to cost a reasonably substantial figure (set out in schedule 2 of the improvement grant section of the Red Book), instalments of the grant up to 90% of the estimated total grant may be paid if the GP requested this when applying and the agreement has been completed.

Before an instalment of the grant can be paid, the FHSA will need to see an architect's certificate showing the cost of the project at the date of the certificate. The instalment payment will be the approved proportion (i.e. 33% to 66%) of the approved costs incurred.

When work is completed and the GP has made all payments, payment of the grant should be claimed on a form obtainable from the FHSA. When returning the claim form, the doctor should also send all receipted bills, details of the cost of any ineligible items and documents to substantiate any additional costs. The FHSA may arrange for an officer to visit the practice to see the improvements before making the final payment.

Grants and tax allowances

The costs of work cannot qualify for both an improvement grant and a tax allowance. It is for a GP, on the basis of an accountant's advice, to decide whether it would be more advantageous to claim a tax allowance or a grant. However, if part of an 'improvement' project does not qualify for a grant, the GP can seek tax relief on the residual costs.

Transitional arrangements

Doctors who at 31 March 1990 had obtained from their FHSAs a formal offer of grant or an equivalent commitment need take no further action unless there is a change in their circumstances, in which case they should inform their FHSA without delay.

Representations

If a GP disagrees with an FHSA's decision that a project is ineligible for grant, representations may be made to the Secretary of State, setting out the reasons for dissatisfaction.

Cost rent

General provisions

A GP may opt for reimbursement of surgery 'costs' based on the cost of providing separate purpose-built premises, or their equivalent, instead of current market rent. This reimbursement is known as a 'cost rent'.

Under this scheme the FHSA must, as well as using the discretion it is allowed, bear in mind its current policies and cash allocation. Consequently it is possible that a GP might not be offered any reimbursement under the scheme.

If an application is approved under the scheme, reimbursement may be offered subject to a definite timescale within which it has to start.

Doctors who on 31 March 1990 were receiving a cost rent payment or who had already obtained from their FHSA a formal offer, including an interim cost rent calculation, and a target date when reimbursement would be made, need take no further action unless there is a change in their circumstances, in which case they should tell the FHSA.

In calculating the final cost rent, the unit cost limits shown under band 1 of the cost limit schedules or those applying on the date tenders were accepted, whichever are lower, will apply to all existing commitments for payment after 31 March 1990, and the regional variations shown under bands 2, 3 and 4 will not apply. A project will be accepted as an existing commitment if, before 1 April 1990, a doctor received a written offer from the FHSA and had told the FHSA before that date of his or her intention to proceed.

Any of the following categories may qualify for a cost rent.

1 Building completely new premises.
2 Acquiring premises for substantial modification.
3 Substantially modifying existing practice premises.

The premises may be owned or rented by the GP and the general provisions of the Rent and Rates Scheme, including the requirement for acceptance by the FHSA and the abatement for private practice, apply.

The scheme gives financial assistance to doctors providing premises suitable for general medical services and appropriate supporting services.

When seeking reimbursement of a cost rent, a doctor must, before entering into any commitment, obtain the FHSA's acceptance of the scheme under the Rent and Rate Scheme, and also a written offer which:

1 states that the proposed project will be acceptable for reimbursement on a cost rent basis;
2 sets out the method for calculating reimbursement;
3 gives a preliminary assessment of that reimbursement (interim cost rent); and
4 gives a target date when the proposed reimbursement may take effect. (If a doctor is unable to comply with a timetable without good reason, the FHSA may withdraw its approval. The doctor would need to reapply if he or she wished to continue with the scheme, and would be responsible for meeting any abortive expenses incurred.)

This written offer enables the GP to decide whether to proceed with the project or modify it. The GP should advise the FHSA of his or her decision in writing.

A GP should ensure that:

1 good advice is received from the outset and the FHSA and its medical adviser are consulted about any proposal to build new or substantially improved premises;
2 an architect is appointed, who is preferably familiar with designing surgery premises and the provisions of the Cost Rent Scheme, in particular the limitations on costs and room sizes;

3   planning permission is obtained from the Local Authority before any substantial financial commitment is taken on;
4   he or she bears in mind, when arranging finance, that the prescribed percentage (*see* pages 138 to 139) which will be applied to the accepted building cost, and the unit costs applicable, will be those prevailing when a tender is accepted or a lease is signed;
5   where a doctor proposes leasing premises under a purchase and lease arrangement, agreement has been obtained from the lessor before any financial commitment is taken on.

Also, a GP should be aware that:

6   reimbursement will be payable from the date on which the premises are brought fully into use for practice purposes.

Terminology

New separate purpose-built premises

Such premises are newly-erected, their design is based on the recommendations contained in the scheme about the overall size of premises, the size of individual rooms and costs, and they are used solely for practice purposes, apart from any incorporation of residential accommodation for a message-taker.

Substantial alteration of premises

It is difficult to explain this term precisely, but any substantial alterations must involve structural work such as extension or modification of a building and:

1   an extension should provide additional accommodation at least equal to the area of a combined consulting and examination room and its associated circulation space, currently defined as 12.5 square metres;
2   for a modification to a building without a proposed extension, the structural work should cost at least the equivalent of the extension referred to in (1) above.

In both cases, substantial alteration must be such as to make the completed premises equivalent to separate purpose-built premises in the view of the FHSA.

Alterations will not qualify for a cost rent even if the cost of the work exceeds the minimum cost specified, unless:

3   the alteration involves the necessary structural work;
4   any additional accommodation is necessary.

Outline approval

This means approval in principle of the proposed scheme, indicating the priority which may be given to it in the FHSA's forward programme, including any provisional estimate of when cost rent reimbursement could be expected, if at all. It does not indicate any firm financial commitment by the FHSA.

Written offer

This a formal offer from the FHSA of cost rent reimbursement, which normally includes an assessment of the interim cost rent. However, an FHSA may give a preliminary cost rent assessment subject to providing a more detailed interim calculation at a later date. *Doctors are advised not to enter into any financial commitment until they have received and accepted a written offer.*

Interim cost rent

This is the figure calculated by the FHSA on the basis of the provisional site value, the cost schedules and the prescribed percentage.

It enables the GP to decide, before entering into any substantial commitment, whether the proposed project is financially sound.

Actual cost of site

This is the amount paid by the doctor for the site; and from 1 April 1989 it includes VAT.

Prescribed percentage

This is the appropriate rate of reimbursement notified to the FHSA by the Department of Health from time to time, and used in calculating the final cost rent payable. It is determined as follows.

1   For owner-occupiers, the prescribed percentage will be the rate of interest on the date when the GP accepts the building tender for the project. The appropriate rate will be the variable reimbursement rate notified by the Department except that:

(i) if the GP is financing a scheme wholly or mainly on a fixed rate basis, the prescribed percentage will be the fixed reimbursement rate;

(ii) if the GP is financing a scheme wholly or mainly through a fixed loan but with the option to switch to a variable interest rate loan, the prescribed percentage will be the fixed rate unless and until the GP opts to switch to a variable rate, in which case the prescribed percentage will be the variable rate as from the date when the variable rate takes effect;

(iii) if the GP is financing the scheme wholly or mainly from his or her own funds, the prescribed percentage will be the fixed reimbursement rate.

If the prescribed percentage is the variable reimbursement rate, the final cost rent will be subject to alteration later in line with changes in the variable reimbursement rate.

2   If a GP leases premises from a third party, the prescribed percentage will be the Department's fixed reimbursement rate prevailing on the date the GP signs the main lease. Where lease premises are subsequently extended, the prescribed percentage on the extension will be determined on the date the lease on the extension or the amended lease on the extended property is signed.

To help the FHSA to determine the appropriate rate of interest for the determination of the cost rent, a GP should tell the FHSA in writing, before the date tenders are signed, how the scheme is to be financed. Occasionally, financial arrangements may not be finally settled at that time; if so, the GP should tell the FHSA as soon as they are known, and certainly no later than 6 months after signing the contract.

Final cost rent

This is a figure based on the cost of the project finally approved by the FHSA. The approved cost will be the costs incurred, providing these are allowable under the scheme and do not exceed its total cost limits. The actual cost rent will be calculated by applying the prescribed percentage to the approved cost.

Where the appropriate prescribed percentage is the variable reimbursement rate, the cost rent payable will be varied by the FHSA subsequently from the date of each change in that rate made by the Department.

Schedule cost (unit cost limit)

The schedules in the Red Book indicate the limits, excluding the cost of the site, on payment by the FHSA for new separate purpose built premises and are intended to make generous provision for a good standard of accommodation. The schedules are reviewed annually and amended when necessary to reflect changes in building costs. For owner-occupied premises, the determining date for schedule costs is the date the tender is accepted, and for leased premises it is the date the main lease is signed.

Actual rent

This is the rent actually paid by a GP to his or her landlord.

Operative date for reimbursement

This is the day on which the new or altered accommodation is first brought fully into use by the practice.

Current market value of site

This is the value of the site on the open market, on the assumption that it is available for development for any purpose for which planning permission might reasonably be forthcoming.

Third parties

For the purpose of the scheme third parties exclude:

1   members of the GP's family;
2   private companies of which he or she, or any of his or her partners, or a member of his, her or their families is a shareholder. (After 31 March 1990, an application involving such a company will only qualify for exemption if the doctor or partner or family member individually or collectively holds a majority of the shares);
3   charitable trusts established for the relief of sickness or the preservation or protection of health, of which part of the trust's activities may be to make available surgery premises to GPs at a full commercial rate for use as a surgery.

For all these exclusions, similar conditions apply as for doctor owner-occupiers.

General guidance

Siting of premises and standards

Advice on standards of accommodation is given in paragraph 56/schedule 1 of the Red Book. When choosing a site for new premises, a GP should bear in mind the possibility that extra expense may be incurred because of site conditions. For instance the site may be uneven, marshy, or have suspect subsoil strata.

Application should then be made to the FHSA for outline approval of the proposed project. The FHSA will indicate whether the proposal is compatible with its priorities for premises and is acceptable under the scheme, and will give a provisional estimate of when cost rent reimbursement can be expected if at all.

The FHSA will be prepared to consider an additional allowance if a site which involves exceptional expenditure on site work has necessarily been chosen.

Before a site is purchased, a GP should ensure that planning permission, or at least outline permission, for practice premises will be available from the Local Authority.

As much information as possible about the site should be obtained and sent to the FHSA. This should include the price; plans showing its area; the tenure, whether freehold or leasehold; and if leasehold, the ground rent and length of lease. The FHSA and District Valuer also need to know of any restrictive convenants on the site, any easements, rights of way, fixed charges, or any special outgoings other than normal rates or taxes. The District Valuer will only be able to give a valuation if all the relevant information concerning the site is provided.

If a site larger than that needed for the practice premises is acquired, reimbursement will be based on the total site cost (or the District Valuer's valuation, whichever is lower), but the FHSA will encourage the doctor to dispose of any excess land.

Architect's sketch plans

Architect's sketch plans should be prepared, showing the dimensions of the premises and the individual rooms, and indicating the proposed use of each room, and should be sent to the FHSA.

Self supply and VAT registration

After 1 August 1989, any doctor developing new premises where the project has a total cost (including land) of more than £100 000 must register for VAT. Self supply occurs when a doctor supplies premises to himself or herself, on completion of the project or on first occupation, whichever is earlier. The doctor is classed as a developer of new premises, and the self supply is subject to VAT at the standard rate.

A doctor or partnership must apply to the local VAT office for registration within 30 days of the self supply, else a financial penalty can be imposed. However, if the registration occurs at the start of the development, cash flow can be improved by recovering the VAT paid out to contractors and professional advisers.

It is essential to seek advice from an accountant, both on the registration process and on the completion of quarterly VAT returns. The returns must be submitted on time as there are penalties for late submission. VAT paid out on the project during development, including that incurred on services received up to 6 months prior to registration, can then be recovered. This will include VAT paid on the land cost as well as on goods and services, but not any tax paid in connection with the provision of health care.

At the time of the self supply, VAT must be paid on the total value of the project. After all the VAT paid out on the project has been reclaimed, the doctor or partnership should then deregister. In the final analysis, VAT will have been levied on all the costs of the project at the standard rate.

Action by the FHSA

Site

The District Valuer will give the FHSA an assessment of the current market value of the site.

The cost schedules

The cost schedules (paragraph 51/schedule 1 of the Red Book) indicate the limits on payment by the FHSA for new separate purpose-built premises or their equivalent. The limits are inclusive of VAT but exclude site cost. The schedules are intended to provide for a good standard of practice accommodation and are based on a practice unit which varies according to the numbers of doctors consulting at one time. The number of consulting suites need not be the same as the number of doctors in the practice.

If a trainee practitioner is regularly employed, an additional suite can be provided for that doctor but will not be accepted as part of the practice unit. The cost factor relating to the optional additional room formula will be used in working out the cost rent.

Additional rooms will also be allowed for attached staff such as district nurses and health visitors at the discretion of the FHSA.

Variations from recommended sizes

Doctors may, if they wish, build premises larger than the limits laid down in the schedules but the cost limits for building will not be increased.

FHSAs may also agree to areas smaller than those specified in the schedules provided that the individual rooms conform to the minimum size standards.

However, if established buildings are modified, FHSAs will exercise discretion in applying cost limit reductions if the room sizes and the overall size of the building differ from the schedule figures because of the dimensions of the original building.

Calculation of cost limits

To calculate the notional cost of the building work, FHSAs compare the area of the practice units proposed in the plans with the appropriate area set out in the schedule. No account will be taken of minor differences, but the cost limits for the practice unit will be increased to take account of training facilities and reduced if the area proposed is smaller by 5% or more than the area in the appropriate schedule. Paragraph 51.52.13 of the Red Book explains how this is done.

To the cost of the practice unit, FHSAs add the cost of any optional additional rooms, and to the aggregate of both a percentage is added to cover external works, the preparation of car parks etc., site works and off-site works. To the aggregate of all these figures is added a further percentage for professional fees. The cost limit is subject to regional variations shown in schedule 1 of paragraph 51 of the Red Book, and each FHSA area is allocated to one of four bands which reflect variations in building costs in schedule 3 of paragraph 51.

Message-taker's accommodation

If a GP wishes to include residential accommodation in a scheme which will be occupied by someone, other than a doctor, who takes calls from patients outside surgery hours, the FHSA should be consulted before plans are drawn up. The FHSA may accept such accommodation if it considers it reasonable to do so, and the costs allowed will be those of the optional additional room.

Interim cost rent

The FHSA will advise the GP of the interim cost rent. This will be the prescribed percentage of:

1 the site value, or the market value of the site only when existing premises are to be substantially altered, as assessed by the District Valuer, or the actual site cost, whichever is the lower;
2 the schedule cost or the equivalent to the proposed project.
   The interim cost rent is based on the figures prevailing when the calculation is made. Subsequent changes in the prescribed percentage and the schedule cost will alter the final cost rent.

Subsequent variations

Any significant variations from the information given to the FHSA, for example the sale of part of the site or a change in the plans, must be drawn to the attention of the FHSA for approval and possible recalculation of the interim cost rent.

Tenders

FHSAs will normally expect GPs to provide three tenders for building work. However, where there are difficulties in or objections to obtaining three tenders, two may be accepted, or even one if the prior agreement of the FHSA is obtained.

GPs should seek tenders on a firm price basis and should confirm that quoted items such as prime cost sums are realistic and that reasonable provision is made for contingencies. Firm price tenders, however, will allow increases in costs due to Government action, for example changes in taxation.

If exceptionally a GP is unable to obtain a fixed price tender because the project is expected to take more than a year to complete, the FHSA will consider accepting a price fluctuation clause for cost rent purposes providing it approves this before the building contract is signed.

Current market rent

The cost rent for new or substantially modified premises is an alternative to current market rent. Initially, it is unlikely that the current market rent will produce more favourable reimbursement than a cost rent. Unless a GP feels that current market rent could exceed cost rent, he or she should not ask for an assessment of a current market rent when a new scheme commences. The cost rent will be paid until the GP chooses to change, on a review, to current market rent, or until the premises or a significant part of them cease to be used for practice purposes.

Reviews can be carried out:

1 for premises owned by GPs, every 3 years from the operative date of the cost rent; and
2 for premises leased by GPs, when a review of the rent is due under the terms of the lease or a new lease is entered into at the end of the existing lease.

Improvement grants

It is possible to claim an improvement grant when substantially improving premises through the Cost Rent Scheme. The amount of any grant paid will be deducted from the aggregate cost to which the prescribed percentage is applied.

Unusual projects

Proposed projects which the FHSA accepts as designed to produce the equivalent of separate purpose-built premises, but which are not covered specifically in the Cost Rent Scheme, have to be considered by the Department of Health for advice on how to calculate a cost rent.

Specific procedures

Paragraphs 51.53.1 to 51.57 of the Red Book explain how FHSAs calculate the final cost rent in various circumstances. Two common examples will illustrate how FHSAs make these calculations.

New premises to be owned by the practice

The final cost rent will be calculated on the basis of tenders, receipted accounts, etc., as the prescribed percentage of the aggregate of:

1   the actual cost of the site at the date of acquisition by the GP or its current market value at the date of assessment by the District Valuer, whichever is the less;
2   fees and legal costs arising from the purchase of the site including the legal costs of obtaining a mortgage;
3   the cost, based on the lowest acceptable tender, of the building work (including professional fees) *or* the notional cost for this work based on the appropriate cost limits, whichever is the less;
4   where, before the completion of the premises, loans are obtained to buy the site or to finance progress payments (to the value of the work done as certified by an architect), interest charged on these loans up to the operative date of the cost rent reimbursement.

Substantial modification of existing premises owned by the practice

The final cost rent will be:

either a combination of the reassessed current market rent or the existing rent of the original premises, whichever is the larger, and, cost rent calculated as the prescribed percentage of the aggregate of:

1   the cost of the adaptation (including actual professional fees) and the cost of any additional land or premises acquired by the doctor *or* their value as assessed by the District Valuer, whichever is the less;
2   the statutory cost of passing plans and first inspection of the building;
3   fees and legal costs arising from the purchase of the additional land and premises including, where applicable, the legal costs of obtaining a mortgage; and
4   where, before the completion of the adaptation, loans are obtained to buy additional land or premises or finance progress payments (to the

value of work done as certified by an architect), interest charged on these loans to the operative date of the final cost rent reimbursement;

or the prescribed percentage of the aggregate of:

5   the value of the site and premises at the date of acquisition by the GP as assessed by the District Valuer *plus* whichever is the less of the value of any additional land and premises similarly assessed *or* their actual cost;
6   the appropriate unit cost for new purpose-built premises of the same size as the existing premises after adaptation;
7   fees and legal costs arising from the purchase of the additional land and premises including, where applicable, the legal costs of obtaining a mortgage; and
8   where, before completion of the adaptation, loans are obtained to buy additional land or finance progress payments (to the value of work done as certified by an architect), interest charged on these loans to the operative date of the final cost rent reimbursement;

whichever is the less.

Ground rent

If a site is leasehold, the FHSA should be told when the GP applies for acceptance of the proposals. A copy of the lease showing the ground rent payable should be sent to the FHSA together with other documents submitted when work has been completed.

The ground rent will, except when already included in a current market rent assessment, be added to the above final cost rent calculations.

Purchase and lease

Under a purchase and lease scheme, a bank, building society or other reputable financial institution may acquire from doctors newly-completed, self-contained, purpose-built surgery accommodation or its equivalent, which does not provide for residential accommodation for the doctors and is separately assessed for rating. The financial institution may then lease such premises to the doctors.

Paragraph 51.58 of the Red Book sets out the procedures in detail.

31 Health Centres

THERE are special financial arrangements for GPs practising in health centres. A health centre is defined as premises owned by the Department of Health and managed by the health authority, within which accommodation is provided for GPs. DHAs are responsible for health centres and in consultation with the FHSA will make financial arrangements for their use by GPs.

Charges to GPs

Charges cover:

1 accommodation (i.e. rent);
2 a contribution in lieu of rates and water rates or water meter charges;
3 practice staff employed by the health authority but working for the GPs;
4 services, including heating, hot water, lighting, cleaning, internal repairs and decorations, furniture, moveable equipment, telephones, and the cost of any staff providing these services.

Charges listed under 1, 2 and 3 may be reimbursed directly and are therefore treated separately from those listed under 4.

Box 31.1: Health centre charges

1 Charges are made but fully reimbursed for rent and rates
2 Charges are made but may be partially or wholly reimbursed by the FHSA for any practice staff provided by the health authority. Reimbursement is decided under the terms of the Practice Staff Scheme
3 Charges for services (e.g. heat, light, cleaning) are made, but not directly reimbursed

---

Accounting

Most GPs in health centres arrange to be reimbursed for rent and rates, and the costs of health authority employed staff, at the same time as they incur the expenditure.

Although these costs are directly reimbursed, they still count as outgoings and should be recorded in tax returns, which are available for the Inland Revenue survey of expenses which provides vital evidence for the Doctors' and Dentists' Review Body. At least annually, the FHSA should advise GPs working in health centres of any notional charges due and paid directly on their behalf. GPs must ensure that the first amount continues to be shown gross as expenditure in their accounts, and that the second is shown as income in the same way as capitation fees and any other receipts.

Arrangements for payment

The arrangements for paying health centre costs and charges vary between districts. In some, GPs may pay all these charges directly to the health authority and claim reimbursement from the FHSA. Elsewhere, the FHSA arranges with the DHA that the FHSA should deduct charges from the GP's remuneration (less any reimbursable amounts), and pay these directly to the DHA.

The charge for accommodation (rent)

So that the FHSA can agree with the GPs and the health authority an appropriate level of charges for accommodation, it confirms with the health authority and GPs the amount of accommodation used exclusively or primarily by the GPs and the amount of accommodation, for instance a waiting room, which is used jointly with other users of the health centre. This information may also have an impact on service charges, depending on the method of calculation.

Contribution in lieu of rates

The FHSA and the DHA will use the information agreed about room usage to calculate the contribution due in lieu of rates, which is also reimbursable.

Calculation of accommodation (rent) charges

The District Valuer will assess the current market rent of the GP's share of the accommodation on the basis of the agreed information about usage. The only exception is for certain centres brought into use prior to 1 April 1974, for which a cost rent was calculated. Charges for accommodation are normally reviewed every 3 years.

Ancillary staff

Most GPs in health centres employ their own staff and are reimbursed by the FHSA in the normal way. A health authority should not charge GPs for attached professional staff such as district nurses, midwives or health visitors.

If a health authority provides clerical or administrative staff to perform duties for the GP, the GP will need to agree with the authority the details of the post and the charges to be made. He or she can then claim for reimbursement of those charges under the provisions of the Practice Staff Scheme. There is no longer a guarantee of reimbursement from the FHSA, except for staff covered by provisional arrangements.

Private work in health centres

GPs undertaking private practice in health centres must obtain the Secretary of State's permission to do so through the FHSA. The FHSA needs to know the level of private practice income to determine whether to abate the amounts reimbursed directly for accommodation, rates or staff.

Services

Charges for services are agreed between the GPs and the DHA in consultation with the FHSA. These charges, and those made for staff employed by the DHA, are adjusted if the full cost is greater than that which would be incurred by a GP for similar facilities in privately owned premises locally.

Box 31.2: Service charges

Service charges can be compared with those incurred by GPs practising outside health centres in comparable premises

---

Arbitration

If there is a dispute, health centre charges may be determined by arbitration as provided for in a Health Centre Licence. Even if no licence has been agreed and signed, a health authority will probably agree to the type of arbitration referred to in the Model Health Centre Licence issued in 1977 by the Department of Health and Social Security.

32 Practice Staff

THE new Practice Staff Scheme introduced on 1 April 1990 replaces the Ancillary Staff Scheme, and significantly changes how GPs are reimbursed the costs of employing practice staff.

GPs must understand how this new scheme works, since failure to do so may lead a GP to employ staff for whom little or no reimbursement is received from the FHSA. Many of the rules of the previous scheme, which guaranteed reimbursement, have been removed. FHSAs have been given much greater discretion in operating the new scheme, particularly as to the categories of staff which can be approved and the levels of reimbursement.

Under the new Practice Staff Scheme, there is no longer a definition of 'qualifying staff', and thus a GP may claim payments for a wider range of staff, including for example physiotherapists, chiropodists, dietitians, counsellors, linkworkers or translators. There is now no limit on the numbers of staff for which claims can be made, and no bar on reimbursement of the costs of relatives and dependents employed as practice staff.

The FHSA will publish its policies on the use of its cash limited resources for practice staff and thus inform GPs of its priorities and the likelihood of a particular post attracting reimbursement. FHSAs are required to prepare their policies with the health needs of patients as a key factor in determining how resources are targeted.

General provisions

The scheme provides for direct reimbursement at the FHSA's discretion, of all or part of the expense of employing practice staff (excluding those employed to undertake medical duties such as GP trainees and assistants); any balance of expenditure on staff will as at present, be reimbursed indirectly to the profession through the expenses element of gross fees and allowances.

The FHSA exercises its discretion according to the parameters described below. The FHSA must operate the scheme within an annual cash limit set by the Department of Health. In some circumstances an FHSA may decide not to provide any reimbursement for a particular post.

Important transitional arrangements apply to staff in post on 31 March 1990, the day before the introduction of the new scheme.

Eligibility

All practitioners in general medical practice, including these providing restricted services or with limited lists, are eligible to receive reimbursement at the discretion of the FHSA.

Payment

Payment may comprise the direct reimbursement of any proportion of any one or more of the following practice staff costs:

1 practice staff salary;
2 gross National Insurance contributions paid by the employer (i.e. the total sum due before deducting any employer's NI refund for Statutory Sick Pay (SSP) and Statutory Maternity Pay (SMP));
3 contributions paid by the employer to the NHS Superannuation Scheme, or an approved private superannuation scheme;
4 cost of providing practice staff training, including course fees and travel and subsistence expenses;
5 certain amounts paid to an agency including a health authority (though no payment will be made for an agency's administrative or overhead costs);
6 the balance between the total payment due under the Employment Protection (Consolidation) Act 1978 and any rebate paid by the Department of Employment, where a GP is required by the Act to make a redundancy payment to an employee for whose salary costs have been reimbursed prior to dismissal. (However, the FHSA will normally withhold payment towards these costs if a GP acted without due regard to the FHSA's responsibilities.);
7 payment of salary for reasonable periods of paid holiday, sick leave, maternity leave and training, but excluding the amount of any payment made under the SSP or SMP schemes;
8 payment of salary for relief staff (which may include practice staff covering for absent colleagues) employed to cover staff during holidays, sick leave, maternity leave and training.

Definitions

Salary: the gross amount of the basic pay before deductions for income tax, National Insurance, any superannuation or private pension scheme or plan, but excluding the amount of any SSP or SMP payments. It does not include overtime payments or emoluments in kind, but can include payments for covering other staff.

Post: an appointment which, once approved by the FHSA, will normally continue to be reimbursed at a similar level unless the FHSA finds a significant change in local circumstances on review. This does not, however, prevent GPs from seeking approval for short term or temporary posts.

Post-holder: a person appointed to fill a specific post.

Staff training

Claims for reimbursement of training costs must have prior approval. Costs may include the approved proportions of course fees and travel and subsistence expenses. The FHSA will not reimburse the training costs of agency staff (except administrative staff provided for GPs in a health centre by a health authority), or of health authority staff such as district nurses or health visitors attached to a practice.

Applications

Applications may be made for directly employed staff or certain agency staff performing duties for the GP. The FHSA may grant applications in whole or in part, or may refuse applications. The FHSA has discretion to determine:

1 the percentage of salary, salary increase, or any other payment which may be directly reimbursed;
2 the date from which direct reimbursement may be made;
3 minimum qualifications and experience which practice staff may be required to hold;
4 the percentage or reimbursement for the cost of any introductory or continuing in-service training which practice staff may undergo during the period of direct reimbursement;
5 arrangements to renew approvals or any conditions under which approval is given at intervals no more frequent than every 3 years.

An important part of an application and of subsequent reviews will be:

1 a job description setting out responsibilities, roles and objectives;
2 a contract including details of arrangements for salary review, for example any annual scale increments and cost of living increases.

In determining the percentage of salary or other payment to be directly reimbursed, an FHSA is required to take into account various factors, including its service development strategy, its cash allocation, the circumstances of the individual practice – for example any local recruitment or retention problems – and the need to deal fairly with practices in similar circumstances over the years.

When the FHSA indicates what level of reimbursement it will make, it will also explain the arrangements for reviewing the post at intervals no more frequent than every 3 years.

Applications, notifications and claims under the Practice Staff Scheme should be submitted on the forms listed in Box 32.1.

Box 32.1: Practice Staff Scheme forms

Application for prior approval for all new posts	FP/PS1
Application for any increase in the cost of existing staff to be directly reimbursed	
Application for any significant change in the hours or nature of duties of existing staff	
Application for prior approval for reimbursement of expenses for attendance at training events	FP/PS2
Notification of change of post-holder (including details of new post-holder) and dates of commencement and termination of employment	FP/PS3
Notification of change of salary level (in circumstances described in paragraph 52.13)	
Notification of any reduction in the cost to be directly reimbursed, for example reduction in salary levels or hours	
Claims for reimbursement (including claims for attendance at training events)	FP/PS4

Arrangements for existing staff to whom special transitional provisions apply are described below. In all other circumstances, if a GP seeks to increase the total amount to be reimbursed or the level of salary, even when there is no increase in total reimbursement because the cost can be off-set by reducing the number of hours worked, he or she has to apply for prior approval on form FP/PS1. However, the FHSA will have discretion to relax this requirement for prior approval on form FP/PS1 and may only require notification on form FP/PS3. The circumstances could include those where an FHSA notifies GPs of a maximum sum which it will normally regard as a reasonable cost of living increase within which no prior approval on form FP/PS1 is required. In such circumstances, a GP need only submit a form FP/PS1 if he or she wishes to make a case to receive direct reimbursement for an increase above that notified by the FHSA.

GPs should normally apply on form FP/PS1 for direct reimbursement for a particular post in which specified duties are undertaken rather than for an identified post-holder. If the post-holder subsequently changes, there will then be no need to submit a further application unless the GP wishes to seek a higher level of reimbursement to reflect enhanced duties, a change in hours or salary, or if the post remains vacant for more than 3 months.

Applications for approval of direct reimbursement for a post on form FP/PS1 should be submitted no later than 6 weeks before the proposed date of employment, or by such other date as the FHSA may decide. Applications for approval for direct reimbursement of expenses for practice staff training should be submitted on form FP/PS2 as far in advance as possible of the training event. The FHSA will notify GPs of the outcome of their applications as soon as possible.

Notification of the commencement or termination of employment

A change of post-holder, or the commencement or termination of employment of practice staff, should be notified to the FHSA on form FP/PS3 as soon as possible and no later than 14 days after the change.

Submission of claims and payments

Claims for reimbursement should be submitted quarterly on form FP/PS4, within 10 days of the end of the quarter. Payments are normally made quarterly. In the case of directly employed staff, form FP/PS4 should be signed by the employee or employees to whom it relates. For agency staff, a receipted account from the agency should be submitted.

Payments will be abated if more than 10% of a GP's income comes from private practice.

The FHSA may make monthly advances on account of payments due under this scheme.

Accounting

GPs should record total staff expenses as gross expenditure and direct reimbursements as income in their accounts, so that reliable data are obtained in the Inland Revenue's annual survey of practice expenses.

Qualifications

In determining minimum qualifications and experience which practice staff are expected to hold, the FHSA will take into account any standards (e.g. qualifications, experience, aptitude and personal qualities of staff, or in-service training) adopted by either a national professional regulatory body or an organisation awarding recognized vocational qualifications. In the case of administrative and clerical staff, the FHSA may use its discretion; in particular it must take account of qualifications or experience normally expected of staff for whom in-service training may be appropriate, and it may specify a reasonable interval after taking up a post by which a new member of staff should be able to demonstrate essential core competencies appropriate to the job.

Paragraph 52.23 of the Red Book describes the qualifications which may be held by a practice nurse (normally Registered General Nurse), and the extra qualifications which must be held by those employed on additional enhanced duties, for example midwifery, health visiting and district nursing. A practice nurse who is an Enrolled Nurse may undertake only a limited range of duties.

Periodic reviews

All posts approved after 31 March 1990 will be reviewed no more frequently than every 3 years, as will existing posts if the transitional arrangements cease to apply. Although an FHSA has the authority to discontinue reimbursement following a review, it must act consistently and reasonably, taking account of the advantages to the NHS of ensuring the continuity of employment of skilled staff.

Transitional arrangements

If under the Ancillary Staff Scheme prior to 1 April 1990 a GP had already submitted the appropriate form ANC1, ANC5 or RAN 1/1A and the FHSA had agreed to pay for an employee in post at 31 March 1990, there is no need to submit a fresh application form unless the GP wishes to:

1 apply to increase the cost to be directly reimbursed, by increasing hours of employment or the percentage of salary or other costs reimbursed or salary levels (other than any reasonable salary increase which the FHSA has approved, or any reasonable annual scale increment to which the employee is contractually entitled under an agreement made before 1 April 1990 or an increase in employer's National Insurance contributions, or contributions paid by the employer to the NHS Superannuation Scheme or a qualifying superannuation scheme); or
2 apply to modify substantially the duties of the post; or
3 apply for approval for reimbursement of expenses for that employee's attendance at a training event.

Applications in accordance with 1 and 2 above should be made on form FP/PS1, and those relating to 3 should be made on form FP/PS2. In all cases, claims for direct reimbursement should be submitted on form FP/PS4.

For practice staff members in post on 31 March 1990 and for whom the FHSA has already agreed to make reimbursements, there is no requirement to review periodically the direct reimbursement arrangements unless the employee's hours or duties change substantially or the employee leaves. From then on, the direct reimbursement arrangements applying to the successor post-holder will be subject to periodic review. The FHSA will wish to review immediately the case for continued reimbursement in respect of the successor. It is, therefore, in the GP's interest to contact the FHSA before planning to recruit a successor, so that the GP can take account of the FHSA's plans for review.

Practice staff employed by health authorities in health centres

The arrangements for practice staff employed by health authorities in health centres are considered in this book on pages 148 to 149 in the chapter on health centres.

Summary

The introduction to this chapter emphasizes the importance of understanding how this new scheme works. The new contract contains many changes but those in the scheme for reimbursing the cost of employing practice staff are particularly crucial for GPs.

A GP must know what can be claimed for, how a case can be justified, and which forms are required. Any GP who disregards these changes could lose money and impair his or her ability to run the practice efficiently with the appropriate range of practice staff.

33 Computer Costs

A proportion of computer costs, incurred by a principal, restricted principal, partnership or group practice after 1 April 1989, can be directly reimbursed under a cash-limited scheme that will run from 1 April 1990 to 31 March 1993. The costs of purchasing, leasing, upgrading and maintaining a computer system, and the initial staff costs of setting up the system, are included in the scheme, and the balance of expenditure is reimbursed indirectly. Valid claims which are not considered in one financial year because the available funds are fully committed can be resubmitted the following year.

Definitions

Hardware is defined so as to include computers and their associated equipment, but exclude any computer which is an integral part of another piece of equipment, single-function word processors and telephone lines, except dedicated lines linking computers in main and branch surgeries.

Software means computer programs principally used for practice administration and the delivery of patient care.

Upgrading means enhancing the function of an existing system so as to improve patient care or administrative efficiency.

Expenses covered by the scheme

System purchase costs

If the full cost of system purchase and installation falls to the practice, hardware and software costs can be directly reimbursed up to 50% of the cost or a sum defined in a sliding scale related to list size, whichever is the less. If a GP who has been leasing subsequently purchases a new system, the maximum amount of leasing and purchase costs which can be directly reimbursed is defined by the same sliding scale.

Leasing costs

Up to 50% of leasing costs may be directly reimbursed, up to a ceiling defined in a sliding scale based on list size. Practitioners who receive payments from their system suppliers, including payments for services or information supplied, are excluded from this part of the scheme.

Upgrading costs

If the full cost of the upgrade falls to the practice, a proportion of the hardware and software costs may be directly reimbursed, whether the existing system is owned, rented or leased under any arrangement. The reimbursements of the costs of purchasing a computer system and an upgrade, or of leasing a system and purchasing an upgrade, or of leasing both, are subject to upper ceilings defined according to list size.

Maintenance costs

A proportion of the separately invoiced costs of maintaining the hardware and software of a computer system can be reimbursed, irrespective of when the system was purchased. Where maintenance is included in a leasing agreement and not separately identified, and reimbursement is paid under the heading of leasing costs, no additional payment is due. The payment made is of 50% of the actual costs, or a sum defined in a sliding scale based on list size, whichever is the less. GPs who receive payments from the system supplier in respect of the lease payment or any service or information supplied are not eligible to claim maintenance, except where the maintenance cost relates to upgrades for which direct reimbursement has been received.

Staff costs

Payments may be made of part of the staff costs incurred in setting up a computer system. The payment is of 70% of the actual costs, or a sum determined by a sliding scale related to list size, whichever is the less. The costs cannot also be claimed under the Practice Staff Scheme.

Claims

Claims for system purchase costs are submitted on form CM1; those for leasing costs on form CM2, either annually or monthly depending on how often the costs are incurred; claims for upgrading are sent on form CM3; those for maintenance costs on form CM4, either annually or monthly depending on when payments are made; and claims for staff costs are submitted on form CM5. Appropriate documents should be sent with each claim: a receipt for purchases and upgrades; leasing and maintenance agreements for leasing and maintenance claims; and a contract of employment, stating the job description, period of employment and salary paid, with staff cost claims (*see* Box 33.1).

Box 33.1: Computer cost claims

Costs claimed for	Form	Additional documents required
Purchase costs	CM1	Receipt
Leasing costs	CM2	Leasing agreement
Upgrading costs	CM3	Receipt
Maintenance costs	CM4	Maintenance agreement
Initial staff costs	CM5	Employment contract

Because the scheme is cash-limited, the FHSA has discretion to take into account such matters as the effects of computerization on patient care and administrative efficiency, and the need to apply consistent criteria to different practices. GPs are advised to consult the FHSA before submitting claims.

Representations

If a GP disagrees with an FHSA's decision on an application or claim, representations should be made to the Secretary of State within 2 months.

34 Transitional Payments Scheme

General

This scheme provides for payment to be made to unrestricted principals in practice on 31 March 1990 with small list sizes but receiving BPA who, after 1 April 1990, are unable to maintain or improve their income under the new remuneration arrangements without increasing their list size.

Initially the scheme will last for 2 years from April 1990. The level of payments will, in each case, be reduced by 50% in 1991–92, after which the scheme will be reviewed.

Eligibility

The schedule to this paragraph in the Red Book sets out the levels of payment for unrestricted principals. Eligibility depends on:

1 partnership average list size;
2 whether on 31 March 1990 the doctor was receiving Vocational Training Allowance (VTA) or Group Practice Allowance (GPA);
3 the level of seniority payment (if any) to which the doctor was entitled on 31 March 1990; and
4 whether on 1 April 1990 the doctor was receiving deprivation payments in respect of 10% or more of his or her personal list of patients.

Payments

Payment will be made automatically, by the doctor's responsible FHSA, on a quarterly basis. Claim forms are not required. When a doctor leaves the medical list or leaves the practice where he or she qualified for the payment and joins another one, even if the doctor is remaining on the same FHSA's medical list, the payment will cease.

35 Arrangements for Payment

THE responsible FHSA normally makes all payments to which a GP is entitled apart from rural practice payments, which may be made by the FHSA that determines eligibility for the payments even though it is not the GP's responsible FHSA. The responsible FHSA will obtain from any other FHSAs in whose lists a GP or his or her partners are also included the information needed to determine eligibility to receive:

1 basic practice allowance and additions to the allowance;
2 allowance for employment of associate doctors and of locums employed by rural single-handed GPs on study leave;
3 payments during sickness, confinement and prolonged study leave;
4 capitation fees, deprivation payments and child health surveillance fees;
5 inducement payments and initial practice allowances;
6 rural practice payments (except as described above);
7 registration fees and payments for minor surgery sessions and health promotion clinics;
8 target payments for vaccinations and immunizations and cervical cytology;
9 students allowance;
10 payments under the trainee practitioner scheme;
11 doctor's retainer scheme sessional payments;
12 postgraduate education allowance;
13 reimbursements for staff and premises; and
14 reimbursements of computer costs.

GPs should claim the following fees from the FHSA for the locality in which the patient lives or is temporarily residing, or in the case of emergency treatment for the locality in which the treatment was provided:

1 maternity medical services fees;
2 fees for contraceptive services;
3 night visit fees;
4 temporary resident fees;
5 emergency treatment fees;
6 fees for immediately necessary treatment;
7 fees for the arrest of dental haemorrhage;
8 anaesthetists' fees; and
9 fees for vaccinations and immunizations.

The FHSAs receiving the forms check the claims and notify the responsible FHSA of the amounts due for payment.

> **Box 35.1: Arrangements for payment**
>
> All fees and allowances are paid by the responsible FHSA except, in some circumstances, rural practice payments. However, some claims have to be submitted to the FHSA for the locality in which the patient lives

Capitation fees, deprivation payments, child health surveillance fees and practice allowances due to GPs for a quarter will be paid no later than the last day of the quarter in which they are due.

Claims for most item-of-service fees (night visits, vaccinations etc.) are accepted if made within 6 months of the service being provided, or in the case of MMS within 6 months of the expected date of confinement if this is later. Nonetheless, it is in the GP's own interest to submit claims as regularly and quickly as possible.

The FHSA has discretion to accept claims made after the normal period but within 6 years of the service that was provided. The FHSA's decision will depend on the explanation given for the delay in claiming. Only the Secretary of State can exceptionally approve claims after 6 years.

> **Box 35.2: Submission of claims**
>
> 1 Item-of-service claims must be submitted within 6 months of the date the service was provided
> 2 The FHSA has discretion to accept claims made within 6 years

Arrangements for making provisional payments or withholding payments where eligibility to payments is in doubt, are described in paragraph 75.6.

The arrangements for payments to dispensing doctors are described in paragraph 75.7.

If two or more practitioners are practising in partnership:

1 claims for services provided by either or any of the partners may be submitted as a single claim in the name of the partnership;
2 payments may, if the partners wish, be made as a single payment to the partnership.

Advances on account

Advances can be obtained for payments due in respect of capitation fees, child health surveillance, deprivation payments, allowances and certain payments under the Trainee Practitioner Scheme. Advances may be made either:

1 midway in the quarter, when the advance will not exceed half the estimated payments for the quarter; or
2 monthly, when the advance will not exceed one-third of the estimated payments for the quarter.

Advances can also be claimed for rural practice payments, temporary resident fees, rent and rates and practice staff payments.

Advance payments make a major contribution to a practice's cash flow, and GPs should ensure that they claim these and review them regularly so as to reflect increases in practice income.

Box 35.3: Advances on account

1 Advances can be made in respect of most payments from the FHSA, including direct reimbursements
2 Advances improve a practice's cash flow

Fees abolished from 1 April 1990

No fees are paid for cervical cytology tests, or for vaccinations and immunizations given to children under the age of 6, on or after 1 April 1990.

Claims for fees for such services performed before 1 April 1990 should be made within 6 months of the completion of the services. The FHSA cannot make any such payments after 1 April 1991, and the Secretary of State will not authorize any payment on appeal.

36 Representations to the Secretary of State

GENERAL practitioners who are aggrieved by a decision of their FHSA can make representations to the Secretary of State.

A separate appeal system exists for the Rent and Rates Scheme. In other cases, a GP who is dissatisfied with an FHSA's decision concerning remuneration must first place before the FHSA any relevant additional information. If the FHSA does not alter its decision, the GP may then make representations to the Secretary of State. They must be made as soon as possible after receiving the FHSA's final decision. The GP must submit a case to the Secretary of State explaining the grounds on which his or her representations are based.

If a doctor is dissatisfied with an FHSA decision about an application or claim which has been refused on the grounds of the FHSA's management of its cash allocation, representations can only be made on the grounds that the FHSA failed to follow the Red Book procedures or failed to take into account material written evidence.

Box 36.1: Representations

If a GP is aggrieved by a decision of the FHSA, representations may be made to the Secretary of State.

---

37 How the Red Book is Negotiated and Implemented

THE General Medical Services Committee (GMSC), a standing committee of the BMA with full authority to deal with all matters affecting NHS GPs, is the only body that represents all GPs irrespective of whether they are BMA members (although over 75% are). It is recognized as the GPs' sole negotiating body by the Department of Health. The GMSC is responsible ultimately for determining the advice to be given and representations to be made to ministers and government officials. Although the GMSC has final responsibility for determining the policies to be followed in negotiations, these cannot be formulated in a vacuum. It therefore convenes annually (and on other special occasions) a conference of LMC representatives. Over 300 GPs attend these conferences; they are not confined to BMA members because LMCs represent all GPs locally, just as the GMSC does at national level. The resolutions of these conferences are referred to the GMSC and provide the basis of its policy. It is said that the GMSC ignores conference policy at its peril.

In negotiations with ministers and government officials, the GMSC is represented by a negotiating team of 5 members, all of whom are working GPs. These doctors provide a direct input of their everyday experience of general practice into national negotiations, and are assisted by economic, legal and accountancy advisers. There is a regular cycle of general meetings between the GMSC negotiating team and a team of Department of Health officials, and these are supplemented by numerous other meetings to deal with specific matters. The experience of the GMSC's negotiating team has provided the Department of Health with invaluable advice on the practical implementations of its plans for the family doctor service, and LMCs have provided FPCs with equally valuable advice.

Over the years negotiations between the GMSC and the Department of Health have covered a very wide range of issues. In practice, only occasionally has the satisfactory completion of negotiations required amendment of the Red Book, and very rarely indeed amendment of the legal framework of general practice, the NHS Regulatons (which include the GP's terms of service). It is important to note that the Red Book, although a part of the NHS Regulations, can be amended without legislation, whereas the NHS Regulations are parliamentary enactments and thus require legislation to amend their provisions.

Consultation with the LMC: the traditional pattern

Because NHS GPs are independent contractors and not employees, successive governments recognized that special arrangements were required for administering the contracts GPs held with FPCs. Thus, the LMC nominated GPs for appointment by the Secretary of State for Health to serve with lay people and members of the other contractor professions as members of the FPC. The FPC members who were also working GPs brought a particular experience and expertise to the FPC. Through this representation, the day-to-day work of the FPC in its dealings with GPs was firmly based on the partnership principle. The 'partnership principle' referred to an underlying assumption that the LMC and FPC co-operated as equals to ensure that GP services were run efficiently. Consensus and co-operation normally underlie the decisions reached and the manner in which they were implemented. The professional representation on the FPC itself was distinct from, and no substitute for, the process of consultation between the FPC and LMC.

FPCs have been required by statute to consult LMCs on many issues; this is still evident in the Regulations governing the provision of NHS general medical services, the terms of service of GPs and the Statement of Fees and Allowances (the Red Book) (*see* Boxes 37.1 to 37.3). The LMC also continues to play an important part in the 'complaints procedure' and in the investigation of matters relating to professional conduct.

Box 37.1: Examples of references in the Regulations to consultation with the LMC

The LMC is to be consulted:

1 before removal from the medical list of the name of a doctor who has personally never provided services or has ceased to provide services for the past 6 months
2 on temporary arrangements for carrying on a practice
3 where it appears that a doctor is incapable of providing general medical services because of his or her physical or mental condition
4 on the termination of a maternity medical services contract where the doctor and the patient do not agree

---

Box 37.2: Examples of references in the terms of service to consultation with the LMC

The LMC is to be consulted:

1 before the FPC refuses consent or imposes conditions on a doctor's use of a deputizing service
2 before refusing or withdrawing consent to employ an assistant
3 in the inspection of surgery premises

Box 37.3: Examples of references in the Red Book to consultation with the LMC

1 payment of a higher night visit fee
2 acceptance of premises for rent and rates reimbursement
3 the payment of delayed or late claims

The above examples are only illustrative. The extent of past LMC involvement in the day-to-day running of NHS general practice through its participation in the work of the FPC has been evident from the fact that the LMC was specifically referred to in over 20 paragraphs of the Regulations, 10 paragraphs of the terms of service and in over 30 paragraphs of the Red Book.

On many matters on which the FPC consulted the LMC, the two bodies jointly determined what action should be taken, and in this sense 'consultation' meant 'partnership'. The local recognition and representation ensured the efficient provision of general medical services, enabling FPCs to draw upon the goodwill and experience of local GPs. The process of consultation also ensured that the terms of service negotiated centrally by the GMSC and Department of Health were fairly and reasonably applied locally, and that local discretion was properly exercised when implementing nationally agreed terms of service.

This relationship is now undergoing radical change as described below.

The imposition of the 1990 contract

The imposition of new contractual arrangements, together with other managerial changes emanating from the Government's White Paper *Working for Patients*, have created a very different climate of relations between the GMSC and the Department of Health, and between LMCs and FHSAs.

At national level, after many months of consultation, involving a measure of negotiation, the Government imposed new contractual arrangements on an unwilling and hostile profession. In doing so it consciously broke with a long tradition (extending back to the beginnings of the family doctor service in 1913) of proceeding by consensus, introducing contractual changes only after agreement with representatives of the profession. The question that remains to be answered is whether relations at national level between the professions's representatives and ministers and their officials can return to normality in the months and years ahead.

At local level, relations between LMCs and FHSAs are undergoing a permanent and far more fundamental change. Implementation of the White Paper proposals involves a major revision of the structure, management and line of accountability of FHSAs.

The size of FPCs is being reduced; the number of GP members has been cut from seven to one as the terms of office of existing members expire. New general managers have been appointed with responsibility for managing the contractor services. In brief, the role of the FPC is changing from administering to managing the family doctor service. At the same time LMCs are being pushed towards a more defensive 'union' type relationship with their FPCs, and away from the traditional partnership role. Only time will reveal the full effect of these changes.

Appendix 1: Index to the Statement of Fees and Allowances

Appendix 2: List of Abbreviations

BMA	British Medical Association
BPA	Basic Practice Allowance
DHA	District Health Authority
DV	District Valuer
FHSA	Family Health Services Authority
FPC	Family Practitioner Committee
GMC	General Medical Council
GMPS	General Medical and Pharmaceutical Services
GMSC	General Medical Services Committee
GPA	Group Practice Allowance
LMC	Local Medical Committee
MMS	Maternity Medical Services
MPC	Medical Practices Committee
MSC	Medical Service Committee
NHS	National Health Service
NI	National Insurance
SCT	Service Committees and Tribunal
SFA	Statement of Fees and Allowances
SMP	Statutory Maternity Pay
SSP	Statutory Sick Pay
VTA	Vocational Training Allowance

Appendix 3: Parliamentary Regulations Affecting General Practice

England and Wales

General Medical and Pharmaceutical Regulations

S.I.	Effective	Title
1974 No. 160	01.04.74	The NHS (GMPS) Regulations 1974
1975 No. 719	01.07.75	The NHS (GMPS) Amendment Regulations 1975
1976 No. 690	01.06.76	The NHS (GMPS) Amendment Regulations 1976
1976 No. 1407	04.10.76	The NHS (GMPS) Amendment (No. 2) Regulations 1976
1982 No. 1283	04.10.82	The NHS (GMPS) Amendment Regulations 1982
1983 No. 313	01.04.83	The NHS (GMPS) Amendment Regulations 1983
1985 No. 290	01.04.85	The NHS (GMPS) Amendment Regulations 1985
1985 No. 540	01.04.85	The NHS (GMPS) Amendment (No. 2) Regulations 1985
1985 No. 803	01.06.85	The NHS (GMPS) Amendment (No. 3) Regulations 1985
1985 No. 955	01.12.85	The NHS (GMPS) Amendment (No. 4) Regulations 1985
1985 No. 1053	Regs 1, 2, 4, 5(i): 01.08.85 Remainder: 01.12.85	The NHS (GMPS) Amendment (No. 5) Regulations 1985
1985 No. 1712	01.12.85	The NHS (GMPS) Amendment (No. 6) Regulations
1986 No. 381	01.04.86	The NHS (GMPS) Amendment Regulations 1986
1986 No. 916	01.07.86	The NHS (GMPS) Amendment (No. 2) Regulations 1986

S.I.	Effective	Title
1986 No. 1486	Regs 2(ii), (iii): 01.10.86 Remainder: 01.04.87	The NHS (GMPS) Amendment (No. 3) Regulations 1986
1987 No. 5	Reg 2(iv): 01.08.87 Remainder: 01.02.87	The NHS (GMPS) Amendment Regulations 1987
1987 No. 401	01.04.87	The NHS (GMPS) Amendment (No. 2) Regulations 1987
1987 No. 407	06.04.87	The NHS (GMPS) Amendment (No. 3) Regulations 1987
1987 No. 1425	01.09.87	The NHS (GMPS) Amendment (No. 4) Regulations 1987
1988 No. 1106	01.08.88	The NHS (GMPS) Amendment Regulations 1988
1989 No. 1360	25.08.89	The NHS (GMPS) Amendment Regulations 1989
1989 No. 1987	Regs 1, 5(c), 6, 7, 14, 16, 18, 21(a) (in relation to Schedule 1 para. 11), 24(3): 07.11.89 Reg 23: 01.12.89 Regs 3(b) (in relation to Schedule 1 para. 25, Schedule 1C), 4 (in relation to Regs 3A (1) to (10) and (16) and 3B(1) to (10) and (16)) 21(a) (in relation to Schedule 1 para. 9), 21(c), 22 (in relation to Schedule 6): 01.01.90 Remainder: 01.04.90	The NHS (GMPS) Amendment (No. 2) Regulations 1989
1990 No. 801	01.05.90	The NHS (GMPS) Amendment Regulations 1990

Service Committees and Tribunal Regulations

S.I.	Effective	Title
1974 No. 455	01.04.74	The NHS (SCT) Regulations 1974
1974 No. 907	01.07.74	The NHS (SCT) Amendment Regulations 1974
1987 No. 445	01.05.87	The NHS (SCT) Amendment Regulations 1987
1989 No. 1630	01.02.90	The NHS (SCT) Amendment Regulations 1989
1990 No. 538	02.04.90	The NHS (SCT) Amendment Regulations 1990

Other Relevant Regulations

S.I.	Effective	Title
1981 No. 774	01.08.81	The NHS (Linguistic Knowledge for General Medical Services and General Dental Services) Regulations 1981
1982 No. 288	01.04.82	The Health Service Act 1980 (Consequential Amendments) Order 1982
1985 No. 39	01.04.85	The Family Practitioner Committees (Consequential Modifications) Order 1985
1988 No. 866	06.06.86	The NHS (GMPS and Charges for Drugs) Amendment Regulations 1988

Scotland

General Medical and Pharmaceutical Regulations

S.I.	Effective	Title
1974 No. 506	01.04.74	The NHS (GMPS) (Scotland) Regulations 1974
1975 No. 696 (S. 114)	01.07.75	The NHS (GMPS) (Scotland) Amendment Regulations 1975
1976 No. 1574 (S. 126)	04.10.76	The NHS (GMPS) (Scotland) Amendment (No. 2) Regulations 1976
1978 No. 1762 (S. 155)	29.12.78	The NHS (GMPS) (Scotland) Amendment Regulations 1978
1981 No. 56 (S. 7)	16.02.81	The NHS (GMPS) (Scotland) Amendment Regulations 1981
1981 No. 965 (S. 95)	01.08.81	The NHS (GMPS) (Scotland) Amendment (No. 2) Regulations 1981
1982 No. 1279 (S. 152)	04.10.82	The NHS (GMPS) (Scotland) Amendment Regulations 1982
1985 No. 296 (S. 29)	01.04.85	The NHS (GMPS) (Scotland) Amendment Regulations 1985
1985 No. 534 (S. 51)	01.04.85	The NHS (GMPS) (Scotland) Amendment (No. 2) Regulations 1985
1985 No. 804 (S. 72)	01.06.85	The NHS (GMPS) (Scotland) Amendment (No. 3) Regulations 1985
1985 No. 1625 (S. 125)	01.12.85	The NHS (GMPS) (Scotland) Amendment (No. 4) Regulations 1985
1986 No. 303 (S. 22)	01.04.86	The NHS (GMPS) (Scotland) Amendment Regulations 1986

S.I.	Effective	Title
1986 No. 925 (S. 80)	01.07.86	The NHS (GMPS) (Scotland) Amendment (No. 2) Regulations 1986
1986 No. 1507 (S. 118)	Reg 2: 01.10.86 Remainder: 01.04.87	The NHS (GMPS) (Scotland) Amendment (No. 3) Regulations 1986
1986 No. 2310 (S. 171)	Regs 2, 3: 01.02.87 Remainder: 01.08.87	The NHS (GMPS) (Scotland) Amendment (No. 4) Regulations 1986
1987 No. 385 (S. 35)	01.04.87	The NHS (GMPS) (Scotland) Amendment Regulations 1987
1987 No. 386 (S. 36)	06.04.87	The NHS (GMPS) (Scotland) Amendment (No. 2) Regulations 1987
1987 No. 1382 (S. 102)	01.09.87	The NHS (GMPS) (Scotland) Amendment (No. 3) Regulations 1987
1988 No. 1073 (S. 105)	01.08.88	The NHS (GMPS and Charges for Drugs) (Scotland) Amendment Regulations 1988
1988 No. 1454 (S. 140)	07.09.88	The NHS (GMPS) (Scotland) Amendment (No. 2) Regulations 1988
1988 No. 2259 (S. 221)	01.02.89	The NHS (GMPS) (Scotland) Amendment (No. 3) Regulations 1988
1989 No. 1883 (S. 135)	01.12.89	The NHS (GMPS) (Scotland) Amendment Regulations 1989
1989 No. 1990 (S. 139)	01.04.90	The NHS (GMPS) (Scotland) Amendment (No. 2) Regulations 1989
1990 No. 883 (S. 116)	01.05.90	The NHS (GMPS) (Scotland) Amendment Regulations 1990

Service Committees and Tribunal Regulations

S.I.	Effective	Title
1974 No. 504	01.04.74	The NHS (SCT) (Scotland) Regulations 1974
1974 No. 1031 (S. 88)	15.07.74	The NHS (SCT) (Scotland) Amendment Regulations 1974
1988 No. 878 (S. 87)	01.06.88	The NHS (SCT) (Scotland) Amendment Regulations 1988

Index